THE POWER OF

TIME PERCEPTION

THE POWER OF TIME PERCEPTION

CONTROL THE SPEED OF TIME TO MAKE EVERY SECOND COUNT

Jean Paul A. Zogby

Time Lighthouse Publishing,
London, New York, Dubai

ISBN 978-0-9957347-7-7

Time Lighthouse Publishing
Southwell Gardens, London, U.K.

Printed in the United Kingdom. First Printing, 2017

For information about special discounts available for bulk purchases, sales promotions, fund-raising and educational needs, contact Jean Paul Zogby at jp@jpzogby.com

Free Supplementary Content for Readers

The **Online Speed of Time Test** that measures how fast time runs inside your mind is now available for **FREE for a limited time only.** Click below to get **FREE** Access

http://www.subscribepage.com/speed-of-time-test

You can also download a **FREE** copy of the **Ultimate Guide to a Healthy Brain Diet**, to maintain an alert brain capable of slowing down time.

To download your **FREE** copy, please visit the author's website at http://www.jpzogby.com or http://www.subscribepage.com/brain-diet

To Mom, for all your sacrifices and infinite love.

To Dad, for making me who I am. How I wish you were here.

To my wife and love of my life Roula, I am so lucky to share my life and love with you.

To my children Stephanie, Chloe, and Anthony, you provide me with a constant source of joy and pride. You will inherit the world and make it a much better place.

Special Dedication by David Hampton

Because of the ever quickening passage of years in my own life, I began to reflect upon a time when the days seemed much longer. I remembered the summers between school years that lasted forever. Back then, life consisted of studying various fields of science and electronics for the sheer joy of it. I could barely contain my excitement over the new discoveries that I made on a regular basis. It felt wonderful to spend most of my waking hours doing exactly what I loved and desired most.

In an attempt to get back some of the "wonder" that existed in my earlier years, I began reading articles about the perception of time. The fields of neuroscience, psychology, linguistics, and others came to into view. I became familiar with the names, Karl Ernst von Baer, Gustav Theodor Fechner, and Ernst Pöppel. New language and phrases presented themselves, such as "The specious present" and "Vierordt's law." The effect of neurotransmitters on our own perception of time came to light.

Ultimately, my continuing research, using various phrases and terms in "time perception," led to my discovery of the volume you now have in hand.

This book is not presented as some self-help, quick-fix guide. Although, the information presented is in an easy to digest format. Success ultimately requires being open to adopting some new ways of thinking, such as purposely breaking from life's routines and choosing the less familiar, being more focused on the present and less concerned with the future, as well as learning to resist time pressure.

My hope is that you may come to, more often than not, experience the illusive "Now," induce feelings of "Awe," and have the power to choose the things in your life that really matter to you. At the very least may "The Power of Time Perception" serve as a starting point and guide for your own research and experiments in time perception.

Wishing you a wonderful journey,

David Hampton

TABLE OF CONTENTS

CHAPTER 7

CHAPTER 8

CHAPTER 9

PART THREE

HOW DO WE PERCEIVE THE PAST AND THE FUTURE?

CHAPTER 10

CHAPTER 11

CHAPTER 12

PART FOUR

HOW TO MAKE EVERY SECOND COUNT?

CHAPTER 13

PREFACE

IT WAS LATE SPRING and the last day of school was finally upon us. I was probably around eight years old and, like any school boy at that age, was eagerly awaiting the start of the summer holidays. That school year, like every other school year, seemed like it would never end. With the endless summer days in sight, those last few minutes of the last class seemed to take an eternity. The slow crawling clock hanging on the wall had surely been placed there just to taunt us! Time always seemed to drag when I was waiting for something nice to happen. But then the bell of salvation finally rang and the summer break finally began. Three months of sunny days, fun and adventures.

Do you remember how your childhood summers never seemed to end? For me, it was like an eternity. I grew up in a house situated at the edge of a village in the beautiful Mount Lebanon, overlooking a dense forest of very tall pine and oak trees. We would spend the summer playing in flowery fields, climbing rocks and trees, creeping inside foxhole caves, and following nearby creeks before their streams dried out in the blazing summer sun. The day's adventures would start in early morning and go on until sunset, interrupted only by my mother's call for lunch. At the end of the day, that morning seemed like a distant memory. And so the summer days extended on and on so that, by the time we were back at school, we practically had to learn how to read and write all over again!

Fast-forward 40 years to the present day and I am, again, eagerly awaiting my summer break. This year, like most recent years, flew by so quickly, and I am hoping for a nice long vacation. However, like most vacations these days, two weeks on a beach resort are over in a flash. I return to work, to my daily and weekly routine. The days spent in the office, a couple of evenings at the gym, a night out with some friends, and another for a family dinner. The week is over before you know it and it is time to start all over again. The weeks and months fly by, with each year feeling shorter.

Our perception of the speed of time has always intrigued me. We know from physics that time progresses at the same rate at all times, but that is not how it feels. Time certainly seems to speed up as we grow older. We find ourselves saying things like: 'How is it nearly Christmas again?' 'Has it really been already four years since the last Football World Cup?' There are of course many things other than age that affect our perception of time. Why does time fly when we are having fun and why does it drag when we are bored? Why does time seem to stand still during a car crash accident?

For a long time, the nagging question in my mind has been: is there a way to slow down time to the speed it was running at when we were young? This book is about the psychology of time: how we subjectively perceive time in our lives, not the time as defined by physicists. It is about what seems to speed it up or slow it down; the things we can do to extend a moment of bliss or shorten a moment of pain. It is about how to make a vacation last longer; how to look back at a week, month, or year and be satisfied that it was time well spent. It is about how to slow down life so we can 'live' longer and do all the things we want to do. It is also about the limited time we spend on this rock that is floating in space, we call Earth. It is about those few decades that make up our life and how limited and precious they are. This is the ultimate purpose of this book; to make you aware of your own time, how precious it is, how fast it slips by, and ways to make the most of it.

The drive to write this book started when I got a wakeup call in my early 20s at the passing away of my father to a long fight with cancer. With a family history of cancer running through my uncles and grandfathers, I thought that my turn might come sooner rather than later. I was all the more mindful of this, having grown up during the 16-year Lebanese Civil War in which I had the privilege of brushing with, but surviving, almost certain death on four different occasions. I was among the fortunate ones, but I experienced the horror of seeing some of our closest friends perish. I felt an urge to do something with the limited time I have. I knew that medical science has been advancing the life expectancy at phenomenal speeds. The average human life span for our ancestor cavemen was around 26 years. In 1850, life expectancy was around 44 years. It is currently at 71 years old, and is projected to jump to 97 years by 2050 and even 150 years old by the year 2100! But we cannot obviously wait for that to happen. I wanted to slow down time now and prolong the short life we live. In a certain way, this made me a seeker of science, with a thirst to understand this beautiful world and how it works. As the great Professor Richard Dawkins writes, 'After sleeping through a hundred million centuries, we have finally opened our eyes on a sumptuous planet, sparkling with color, bountiful with life. Within decades, we must close our eyes again. Isn't it a noble, an enlightened way of spending our brief time in the sun, to work at understanding the universe and how we have come to wake up in it?' [1]

This book is about understanding one key aspect of our existence: time. I have spent the last six years researching the subject of time perception, interviewing neuroscientists, covering the latest scientific research in the fields of neuroscience and psychology to understand how we perceive time and what we can do to slow it down. I believe I have found some of the answers and would like to take you on an exciting journey to present, in a simplified manner, what science has to say about our time experience. You will read about some of the fascinating, and perhaps seemingly bizarre, experiments scientists have undertaken to understand time and how we perceive it. These range from putting rats on cocaine, and heating the brain to unbearable temperatures, to pushing students from high platforms, and making them watch nasty spiders! You will explore ways to control your perception of how time flows, ways to use it more efficiently, and how to feel good about it rather than feeling a sense of frustration, or even doom, that it is running out.

The book is divided into 4 main sections. Part 1: 'How Do We Experience Time?' examines how our brains work and the mental systems responsible for perceiving time – the neuroscience of time perception. Part 2: 'What Factors Influence Our Perception of Time?' explores factors that affect the speed of time, such as attention, alertness, emotions, personality traits, and mind-enhancers. You will understand why time goes in slow motion when faced with life-threatening situations, why it drags in boring situations, and why it flies when we are having fun. Part 3: 'How Do We Perceive the Past and the Future?' explores how our experience of the past can result in time distortions when compared to our present experience. We will also cover our experience of the future, mental time travel, anticipation, the mistakes we tend to make when planning things, and more importantly, why time seems to speed up as we grow older. The final Part 4: 'How Can We Make Every Second Count?' offers practical ways for slowing down our experience of time and making next year the longest ever.

It is natural to feel threatened by or helpless towards things we do not understand or cannot control. However, if we learn how to control our sense of time, it will no longer be our enemy. My hope is that by the end of this book, you will have the knowledge to, in the words of the great poet Rudyard Kipling, "fill the unforgiving minute with sixty seconds worth of distance run." After all, we only live once and the least we can do is attempt to make every second count.

Introduction

How Do We Think About Time?

'One life - a little gleam of Time between two Eternities'
— Thomas Carlyle

More Precious than Gold

What comes to mind when we think about time? Why time is so precious and why do we seek ways to 'make the most of it'?

Let us go back to 4,000 BC in ancient China where the first clocks were invented. To demonstrate the idea of time to temple students, Chinese priests used to dangle a rope from the temple ceiling with knots representing the hours. They would light it with a flame from the bottom so that it burnt evenly, indicating the passage of time. Many temples burnt down in those days. The priests were obviously not too happy about that until someone invented a clock made of water buckets. It worked by punching holes in a large bucket full of water, with markings representing the hours, to allow water to flow at a constant rate. The temple students would then measure time by how fast the bucket drained. It was much better than burning ropes for sure, but more importantly, it taught the students that once time was gone, it could never be recovered.

Of course, with the advancement of technology, no one uses water clocks anymore. But the fact that time is so limited remains ever true. Time is our most precious possession because, as with the burning rope or water clock, once it is consumed it cannot be replenished. No matter how much we hate to admit it, it will eventually run out. While you can always work more hours to earn more money, you cannot do anything to gain more time. It is such a slippery resource that is only visible when it passes and only valued when it is gone. Unlike money that can be saved in a bank, or gold that be hidden in a treasure box, time cannot be saved. We have no choice but to spend every moment of it; and every moment that is spent is a moment that is gone forever.

Given that time is more precious than money, it seems entirely irrational that many of us are more willing to spend our time in making more money, but are reluctant to spend more money in enjoying our time. We look for the best bargains and think twice before spending our money 'wisely', but often fail to do the same with time. 'Wasting' a couple of hours is not as bad as losing a couple of hundred dollars from our wallet, even though in reality, time is far more precious than money. We all have that tendency to spend time as if it costs us nothing and it gets worse when you consider that time has an additional 'opportunity cost' attached to it. You can divide your money and spend it on various things, like clothes, a new car, or a fancy dinner, but you can only spend your time on one thing at a time. When you spend time on a certain activity, you effectively give up the opportunity to spend it on other things for the activity you chose. Any benefit that might have been derived, had you chosen to do any of those other things, would be lost forever.

Time is also priceless because it is truly a miracle that we are here. The odds that we are alive at this moment in time are one in a billion zillion. Think about it, there was only one chance in all of the history of this universe that you would have been able to exist, and there you are, you made it. If for any reason your father and mother, or any of your grandparents, did not meet at exactly the right time, and at exactly the right place, you would not be here. If any of your ancestors, having gone through wars, famines, pestilences, and all kinds of fatal calamities, did not manage to survive, you would not be here. The odds are astronomically stacked against your existence, but you won the lottery of life, only you do not know that you won and the prize value in the time given to you is kept hidden. You spend from that credit line without knowing the remaining balance. You realize that whatever you spend cannot be replenished and that lottery of life can only be won once, never twice.

Yet, life is relatively short and old age creeps up fast. Before you know it, the grand theatre of life drops down its curtains for the final exit. That seems a bit unfair. If it took such an enormous effort for the universe to get us here, and against staggering odds, why would it only allow us to stay for a relatively short while? "It takes billions of years to create a human being, and only a few seconds to die", wrote Jostein Gaarder. We all know that death brings about the end of our own time. However, that reality is mentally and emotionally difficult to comprehend. In his Pulitzer Prize winning book, *The Denial of Death*, Ernest Becker declares that the fear of death is at the heart of the human condition. We all try to deny it. 'We live our life as if we are never going to die and die as if we never lived', says the Dalai Lama. But it is not wise to deny that our time will one day come to an end, for that will lead us to undervalue our present time. In case of such denial, we might not care how much time has already elapsed and go ahead and waste time as if we have an unlimited supply, not knowing that tomorrow may be our last. If, on the other hand, we view time as limited and scarce, everything will take on a different dimension and we will place a greater value on the things we do here and now. Every minute that we spend with a loved one, for instance, becomes infinitely more precious; and every hour that is wasted becomes a great unrecoverable loss.

'The odds are astronomically stacked against your existence, but you won the lottery of life, and you made it'

The Value of Time: Work and Leisure

The value we give to time also depends on the amount of free time we manage to extract from our daily routine and devote for leisure. Inventions and technological achievements of the past 100 years were all made for the purpose of saving time and providing people with more leisure time. Cars and planes were invented to make trips shorter. The computer was developed to make work easier and faster. Phones were devised to make communications faster. So many machines - washing machines, dishwashers, microwaves - have been designed to save time. Back then, people thought that in the future everyone would have nothing to do. The 19th century British economist, John Maynard Keynes, imagined that in 1930 'our grandchildren would work around three hours a day.' In his day, technology had already reduced working hours and there was no reason to believe that trend would not continue. In fact, according to recent statistics, Americans work 12 hours less each week than they did 40 years ago, and it is even less in Europe.

The main problem that social scientists had to tackle seemed to be: what can people do with all that free time? It cannot obviously be placed in a 'Time Bank' for future consumption, nor can it be passed on to our children or to some friend who is short of time. But free time did not turn out to be a problem after all. A look at how people spend their time nowadays reveals that people are busier than ever. Time scarcity has in fact increased, especially in the corporate world, and particularly among working parents. It turned out that the problem is less about how much free time we have and more about how we perceive that time. And this all started with the Industrial Revolution of the 18th century, when clocks were used to measure labor and the value of time became associated with money. Due to this association, the more valuable we perceive our time to be, the less eager we are willing to 'waste it' on leisure and the scarcer it will seem.

In a recent study that was carried out at the University of Toronto, two groups of people were asked to listen to the same piece of music, *'The Flower Duet'* from the opera *Lakme*. One group was asked to calculate their hourly wage before the song started while the other group was not asked. The participants in the group who had made the calculation felt less happy and more impatient, while the music was playing. They felt that listening to that music was a waste of time that could have been spent in a more profitable way. The study showed that most people tend to avoid wasting time so as to maximize the money that they can generate. The additional free time that technology has freed up is often not spent on enjoying life but on more work and money-hoarding. And though people may be earning more money to spend nowadays, they are not earning more time to spend it in. The higher the paycheck, the scarcer time seems and the more rushed people become.

Wasted Time?

We all seem to be running after something, trading our time for money and all sorts of things, but for what? Given that time is our most precious resource, we have to consider to what extent is the exchange worth it? You have probably heard the saying that money cannot buy happiness. An interesting 2009 Gallup survey conducted over a period of two years and which gathered 450,000 responses concluded that people are happier and more satisfied with their life as their annual income increased. However, when annual income passed above 75,000 U.S dollars, life-satisfaction continued to increase but happiness did not improve any further. Earning more than that income threshold did not contribute further to people's emotional well-being [2]. If the purpose of life is to be happy, than this implies that on average, spending time on earning more than 75,000 U.S dollars is time that is not well-spent as it does not make us happier. A central question is therefore this: are we making the most of our limited time? How much time is unnecessarily wasted on things that are not beneficial to our life fulfillment and emotional well-being? Of course, defining 'wasted time' is largely subjective; and there is a saying that 'time you enjoy wasting is not wasted time'. However, we will later explore in more detail that there are certain activities that are considered optimal for life fulfillment. It will suffice to note for now that these are the type of activities where people experience 'being in the zone' or 'in the flow'. Spending time in that state of mind is not only extremely gratifying but also alters our experience of time itself.

For now, let us look a little bit further into the 'value' of time and 'wasted time' as it relates to the culture, country, and the pace of life in the city we live in.

Time & Culture

The culture we grew up in affects how we view time, the value we place on time, and how we spend it. Time is perceived differently by Eastern and Western cultures, between countries of the same culture, and even between cities within the same country. In Western Europe, for instance, people living in Switzerland view time very differently from their neighbors in Italy. In Northern America, the United States and Mexico view time in an entirely opposite manner that often causes friction between them. Similar opposing views exist in the East as in, for instance, Thailand and Japan. Let us start with the Western concept of time.

In Western culture, time is viewed as something that is linear. We travel through time on a line. Life is considered a 'journey' and death is the 'end of the road'. The past is something that is behind us and the future is a path that stretches in front of us. Time is an arrow. There is a beginning and an end to everything. This is based on ideas derived from the Semitic religions (Judaism, Christianity and Islam), where the Universe had a clear beginning and will one day come to an end on judgment day. In those religions, humans are born once and die once.

This linear view of time permeates many facets of Western culture. It explains why Westerners tend to be more focused on the future. It allows them to forecast future events, such as quarterly sales projections, through meticulous planning. You can be extremely confident that the train in Zurich will leave at exactly 10:07 a.m. tomorrow morning and arrive at 11:04 a.m. sharp. People in these cultures aim to eliminate future unknowns to their best of their abilities. As a result of this linear view, time is considered very precious and limited in supply.

The linear view also allows for the value of time to be equated with money. If you ever had to deal with an American lawyer or doctor, you would quickly realize that time is money. Americans live in a profit-driven society where time is precious and needs to be quickly utilized as fast as it is passing. To achieve a decent status in U.S. society, you have to make money and you view your time in terms of your hourly wage. To save one million dollars by the age of 30, you would have to earn $100,000 annually, which is around $40 per hour. This is a linear mathematical relationship between time and money. Equating time and money is also why Americans do not generally tolerate idle time and prefer action over 'wasted time'. They look for ways to save time, such as improving efficiencies in factory production.

This view is also shared in Britain and generally the Anglo-Saxon world, along with Switzerland, Germany, the Netherlands, Austria, and the Scandinavian countries where time precision for the sake of reducing wasted time is immensely important. Time is extremely regulated for the Swiss, for instance, who made precision their national symbol. Their watches, optical instruments, transportation, and banking industries stand witness to that. In 1836 Britain, John Belville began to sell time by setting his pocket watch at the Greenwich Observatory where he worked and selling the precise time to clients in London! People living in Anglo-Saxon countries view time as being wasted if it is passing without any decision or actions being taken. They prefer to focus on one thing at a time so that they can efficiently complete more things within a certain deadline. Those countries are influenced by the Protestant work ethic, which associates success with working harder and longer hours. Examples of popular idioms are 'The early bird catches the worm' and 'Never put off to tomorrow what you can do today'.

Contrast that to societies that existed in the Soviet Union, where success is achieved by those who make the most by working the least. The Anglo-Saxon view is also considered naive in Southern European countries, like Italy, Spain, Greece, or the Arab world, where success is often associated with privilege, birthright, and connection to authorities. Time is often viewed as a rubbery flexible thing. People in these countries are generally not very interested in punctuality or setting deadlines, but more on the end result, regardless of how long it takes. A meeting, for instance, is not constrained by clocks but by the discussions themselves and time can be stretched or manipulated to reach a reasonable conclusion. People from these cultures generally feel less rushed. Time runs at a slower pace. While Americans tend to think about time in 5-minute increments, people living in Mediterranean countries and the Middle East do so in 15-minute increments. Popular expressions are 'In Sha' Allah' that you hear often in the Arab world and means 'If God wills', or the Italian proverb

'Since the house is on fire, let us warm ourselves', or the Turkish proverb 'What flares up fast extinguishes soon'.

People in Southern European and Middle Eastern countries tend to be more focused on the present, not the future, which likely is the reason why such countries are behind in planning and are relatively less developed than their northern counterparts. It also explains why people living in Spain, France, and Greece, save less money on average, with Italians being the worst savers, when compared to people living in countries like Britain, Netherlands, and Germany who tend to be more focused on the future and are among the highest savers in Europe. However, this emphasis on the present is also likely why people in Mediterranean cultures appear to enjoy life more, as it is happening now, e.g. the Italian *La Dolce Vita* (the sweet life), and generally prefer smaller immediate gratifications over larger long-term rewards. Now what about the Eastern view on time?

In contrast to the West, time in the East, is viewed as being cyclic. The sun rises and sets, the seasons follow one another, generations follow generations, governments succeed each other, and this goes on forever. Time is more like a boomerang, not an arrow. This idea originates in Eastern religions (Buddhism, Hinduism, and Taoism) that believe in reincarnation. People in cyclical cultures also tend to focus more on the past because they believe they can find many links to what is happening now. People's actions in previous lives, known as karma, determine what type of existence they will have after rebirth.

Unlike their West counterparts, Asians are generally not pressed to make quick decisions but prefer to contemplate and take their time. Time is not a scarce commodity in this view. For them, time does not race away in a linear fashion but comes around again in another cycle when they will be wiser to act on the same opportunities and risks, when they re-present themselves. As a result, they are less disciplined in planning their future and more lenient to go with the natural flow. Popular idioms are the Chinese proverb 'Wise men are never in a hurry' or the Japanese proverb 'A proposal without patience breaks its own heart.'

The Chinese and Japanese, in addition to adopting this hesitant contemplation view of time, differentiate themselves from the rest of the Eastern countries by having a keen sense of time. Punctuality is considered very important. Chinese often arrive to meetings 15 minutes earlier so as to finish on time and maximize efficiency. They appreciate the time being contributed in a meeting, more than any other Asian countries. But they would still take their time for repeated deliberations before the deal is closed.

The Japanese have a similar deep sense of the passing time. This can be observed in the contrast between the rapid pace of Japanese factory workers and the slow easygoing pace seen in Japanese gardens or Japanese music. However, an additional feature of how they view time is how meticulous they are in dividing it. Japanese view time as segmented by tradition. These divisions do not follow Western ideas, where tasks are sequentially allocated to time slots for maximum efficiency, but are more concerned with how much time is given to proper courtesy and tradition. In social gatherings, Japanese have marked beginnings and endings that follow traditional phases. People are expected to conform to the heavily regulated society. This helps in defining where people stand in social and business situations. Exchanging business cards in the first 2 minutes of a meeting is a clear example that marks the beginning of a relationship. Students in Japanese schools are expected to formally request their teacher to start before the lesson begins. At the end of the class, they offer a ritualistic sign of gratitude. The same rituals apply in tea ceremonies, New Year and midsummer festivities, company picnics, sake-drinking sessions, martial arts sessions, and cherry blossom viewings. These activities are experienced by the Japanese in an unfolding manner. For them, time is segmented into slots defined by tradition where it is important to do the 'right thing at the right time'.

In brief, the difference in views on time between the various cultures, being linear, flexible, or cyclic, affects the value people place on time. Depending on the culture you grew up in, you will be more inclined to place a higher value on time, as a scare resource that is running out swiftly, or less value as an abundant resource that will always come back again. This also affects whether you are more focused on the past, present, or future.

The Pace of Life

The value of time, as being limited or abundant, not only changes with the various cultures and sub-cultures, but also varies between countries of the same culture and between cities of the same country. The reason is that the view that time is limited or abundant is intricately related to how fast we feel time is running. And the perceived speed of time depends on the pace of life in the city where you live. In an interesting 1990 study, Robert Levine and his colleagues evaluated the pace of life in 36 American cities by measuring four indicators: the speed with which bank tellers made change, the talking speed of postal clerks, the walking speed of pedestrians, and the proportion of pedestrians wearing wristwatches. Levine found that the Northeastern United States were more fast-paced than the Western United States. Out of the 31 cities surveyed, the three fastest-paced cities were Boston, Buffalo, and New York[3]. The three slowest-paced cities were Shreveport, Sacramento, and Los Angeles. They also found that people living in fast-paced cities tended to focus more on time and on making every minute count, which created more stress. That is why fast-paced cities have higher heart attack death rates and a higher proportion of cigarette smokers.

In 1999, the same researchers carried out another study surveying the largest cities in 31 countries in an effort to determine what factors contribute to the pace of life. They went into each country and measured the pedestrians' walking speed on a clear summer day in downtown areas. They also measured the time it took postal workers to complete a standard request for stamps. They went inside 15 banks and noted the accuracy of their clocks. The results showed that Japan and Western European countries had the fastest pace of life. The pace of life in cities like Tokyo, London, and Paris causes time to run fast, so people tend to feel rushed and under constant time pressure. The United States, Canada, and four Asian economic-growth countries (Hong Kong, Taiwan, Singapore, and South Korea) come in the middle group. Slightly below that were the ex-Soviet bloc countries (Hungary, the Czech Republic, Bulgaria, and Romania), and the slowest pace of life was found in the relatively non-industrialized countries from Africa (Kenya), Asia (Indonesia), the Middle East (Jordan and Syria), and Latin America (El Salvador, Brazil, and Mexico).

Interestingly, the slowest three countries of all were widely associated with a relaxed pace of life. In Brazil, the stereotype of *"amanha"* or "tomorrow" means that, whenever it is possible, people will try to put off today's business until tomorrow. In Indonesia, the hour on a clock is often addressed as *"jam kerat"* meaning "rubber time." And the slowest of all was Mexico, the characteristic land of *"la mañana'*, meaning tomorrow [4]. The researchers also found that the pace of life was slower in hotter cities than cooler ones. This may possibly be due to the fact that in cold cities, natural selection favors people who are more industrious and who keep moving to stay warm. Heat, on the other hand, tends to make people lazier in warmer climates. This could be one of the reasons why northern countries or northern cities tend to be more economically developed then southern ones.

The cause for a fast pace of life in a city is directly related to do with the value people place on time. If we look back at our evolutionary history, we find that, until very recently, time precision was never a critical prerequisite for human survival. In the past, humans only needed to roughly estimate the proper times for eating, sleeping, and working in order to survive. However, nowadays, time is considerably more critical. Aldous Huxley once observed, "To us, the moment 8:17 A.M. means something - something very important, if it happens to be the starting time of our daily train. To our ancestors, such an odd eccentric instant was without significance - did not even exist. In inventing the train, Watt and Stevenson were part inventors of time." As we saw earlier, when time is viewed as money, hours are measured financially, and people worry about wasting time and about how to use it more profitably. With growing economies, time becomes more valuable and seems scarcer. Rich cities, with their higher cost of living, raise the price on people's time. Parisians are more prudent with their time than Mexicans. Pedestrians in Tokyo walk faster than those in Jakarta. In such fast-tempo cities, people earn more money to spend, but do not earn more time to spend it in, making time even more precious. Not having enough time becomes an excuse for not engaging in leisurely experiences, like taking a nice relaxing vacation, enjoying a quiet dinner, or going to a concert or theatre performance. As Erich Fromm put it, 'modern man thinks he loses something - time - when he does not do things quickly. Yet he does not know what to do with the time he gains - except kill it.' The feeling of being constantly rushed affects mental health as well, making people impatient and impulsive. The speed of time that people experience is the culprit.

In one piece of research from Google, it was found that more than a fifth of internet users will abandon an online video if it takes longer than five seconds to load. Time pressure can also lead to an unconscious build-up of stress and has negative health effects such as increased blood pressure and heart disease. It can also cause chronic anger, bitterness, and even a sense of hopelessness. It is also linked to the risk of hypertension, headaches, stomach pain, poor sleep quality, and depression. The overall effect is less happiness and much lower life satisfaction. So what can we do about that? How can we control our perceived speed of time and slow it down to be able to do all the things we want to do?

Physically, slowing down 'real' time is beyond our control. Having a 25 hour day would be great but is not possible (at least not in the immediate future). Just to be precise, I should mention that the duration of a day on Earth is in fact getting longer due to our moon's gravity, which is acting like a brake and slowing down the Earth's spin. As a result, the days are extending by about 1.7 milliseconds each century! At that rate, you will have to wait 140 million years for one day to finally be 25 hours long! I doubt anyone will be there to see that day, let alone make any use of that extra one hour! (And you might have guessed right, it was far worse for the dinosaurs when the Earth was spinning faster, as they had to fit a full day of work in just 23 hours!)

Well, in order to slow down time and maximize our sense of fulfillment, we need to look at how we 'experience' time in our mind, by drawing on the latest findings in psychology and neuroscience and, more importantly, understand why it subjectively seems to pass at different speeds in different situations. We have all experienced moments in life where time 'dragged' or when we were enjoying ourselves how time 'flew'. You might have experienced moments where time froze in situations of extreme fear, such as a car accident. Or you may be currently experiencing a speeding up of time as you are growing older. This speeding up or slowing down of time leads to the stretching or shrinking of time durations and this is not an illusion. To control the perceived speed of time, we need to understand the factors that create this effect in our minds. The pace of life and culture are all external factors that influence how limited or abundant time is viewed. These views can be modified by adjusting the emphasis we put on the past, present, and future and, along with that, our view of time as linear, flexible, or cyclic. But what about the internal factors that affect our time experience? While we cannot control the speed at which real physical time passes (as measured by a good clock), there are things we can do to control how we perceive its passing and, by doing so, we can look for ways to slow it down so as to make every second count The latest research in neuroscience and psychology has given us clues on how to achieve that. As we go through the book, I will propose a variety of practical tips that will help slow down the pace of time, regardless of which culture or city you live in. With that knowledge, my hope is that by the end of this book, you will be able to craft the longest year of your life.

Let us first start with some basics. Our 'sense' of time, what is it and how do our brains think about the present, past, and future?

PART ONE

HOW DO WE EXPERIENCE TIME?

CHAPTER 1

THE PSYCHOLOGY OF TIME PERCEPTION

HOW DO WE SENSE TIME?

'Time has no independent existence apart from the order
of events by which we measure it'
— Albert Einstein

Our Sense of Time

In his famous book, *The Confessions,* written in the year 400 AD, St. Augustine asks, "What then is time? If no one asks me, I know what it is. If I wish to explain it to him who asks, I do not know." We all experience change and motion and we know that these are not possible without time. Although we feel that we have a 'sense of time', our bodies are not equipped with a sensory organ for detecting the passage of time in the same way that we have eyes and ears for detecting light and sound. A table or a chair are objects that exist and can be sensed, but as the eminent French Psychologist Paul Fraisse pointed out, "Duration has no existence in and of itself." Albert Einstein made a similar point that, "Time has no independent existence apart from the order of events by which we measure it." The implication is that time is an inner experience and not a material object of the world. Time it seems is just an illusion!

So how do we sense time? We see shapes and colors, we hear sounds, and feel texture. Yet we know that even if we close our eyes and shut down all our senses, we can still sense the passing of time through the changing pattern of our thoughts. Time is surely then related to the rate of change experienced by our minds. Without change, time would not exist, and everything would happen all at once. More on that later when we explore how our brains perceive change.

Time is therefore an indispensable feature of the way we perceive the world, the way we construct our mental thoughts, and the actions we take. Philosopher Emmanuel Kant spoke of time as a "necessary representation, lying at the foundation of all our intuitions." From the moment of birth, we are immersed in time. All of our actions and experiences evolve in time. We exist in time and our 'sense of time' is critical to everything we do from the mundane act of crossing a road, waiting for a reply, catching a falling object, and managing our working day, to the complex performances by musicians, dancers, and athletes using their sharpened timing skills. Without a proper sense of time, we would not be able to understand and produce comprehensible speech, read and write, focus on a task, switch attention from one thing to another, multitask, sequence the steps to perform everyday tasks, or learn new information. Time is critical to our thoughts, emotions, gestures, and essential to the way we communicate with others. Without the ability to sense time, nothing would make sense.

'Time is related to the rate of change experienced by our minds'

Our sense of time affects our mood when we are waiting in a queue or anticipating an event. If for some reason your brain perceives time as running slower than it really does, you will feel that time is dragging and you become impatient and impulsive in waiting situations. You might start missing your deadlines and will constantly underestimate the time needed to reach appointments. You might cook a dish for 15 minutes instead of the

10 minutes required by the recipe. We all have a sense of time that varies in accuracy depending on various internal and external factors that we will later explore in more detail. A typical example is waiting at a traffic light. When the light goes red, your internal clock starts ticking. Based on your past experience, you do not wait for the orange light to engage gear and go. Your sense of time tells you when you have to do that without any external cues. We all experience time differently, each one in his own unique way, and that experience starts with the perception of the present, that moment in time we call 'now'.

The Illusive 'Now'

We see, hear, feel, and think 'now'. What is experienced is experienced in the present moment. It is a moment in time between a 'no more' and a 'not yet'. You might think that a 'now' moment is instantaneous, having no duration, but it is not. If it was, we would not feel any continuity in the flow of time. Psychologists define the duration of a present 'experienced moment' as just about the longest time interval we can perceive as a whole and still call 'now'. When we experience the flow of time, we do it through an event that is first anticipated, then experienced, and eventually remembered. For instance, when you hear a word in a spoken sentence, you can only understand it in relation to the preceding and succeeding words in the language structure. Likewise, when you are listening to the melody in a song, the *'experienced moment'* corresponds to what is presently in your mind; including the note played just before and possibly, the note expected to follow immediately after. If you are familiar with the Beatles song 'Hey Jude', for instance, the moment you hear 'Hey', you cannot help but hear the 'Jude' already. The 'Jude' is somehow present in your mind even though it is still anticipated in reality. Try it out and mentally sing these two words. As soon as you start with 'Hey', you immediately hear 'Jude' in your mind. Likewise, when you hear 'Jude', the 'Hey' is still somehow present in your memory, even though it is no longer sensed [5]. The first two words of the Beatles song 'Hey Jude' form an 'experienced moment' unit that involves both anticipation and memory. What we experience as the present 'now' is strongly interwoven with what has just happened before and what is about to happen immediately next [6].

This integration of past, present, and future within an 'experienced moment' is what maintains our sense of time continuity. The flow of 'experienced moments' or 'nows' provide the basis of our consciousness and subjective present. They are the fundamental elements that compose the train of our thoughts. So how long is an 'experienced moment'? What is the duration of a present 'now'?

In 1868, German physiologist, Karl von Vierordt became interested in how people are able to guess time intervals of a few seconds long. He observed that people tend to overestimate short intervals and underestimate long intervals. In other words, if you presented a two-second audio clip to a group of people and asked them to guess its duration, most will over-estimate a higher duration, between two to four seconds long. Whereas if the sound clip was eight seconds long, the majority will under-estimate a lower range of between six to eight seconds. It implies that there must be an interim time interval, between long and short intervals, whose duration people can guess correctly. This is called *Vierordt's Law*. Vierordt found that this indifference interval was around 3 seconds. In other words, most people can accurately guess a 3-second time interval, but are unable to do so with much longer or shorter intervals. It is as if the 3-second interval was related to an intrinsic property of our brain that makes it easy to guess accurately [7]. Could this be the duration of our experienced 'now' moment? Another clue comes from optical illusions.

If you have ever seen optical illusions such as Rubin's Vase/ Face, the Necker Cube, or the Boring's Old Woman/ Young Woman Illusion (online examples are easy to find), you may have noticed that these ambiguous figures are essentially static images that have two distinct interpretations. During prolonged viewing, the image in each illusion strikingly changes its appearance to the alternative interpretation in a sudden and unavoidable mental switch. A few seconds later, the brain switches back to the original interpretation and that continues alternating regardless of how hard you try to hold to one interpretation over the other. Brain scientists have discovered that the time between mental switches depends on several factors but is on average around 3 seconds long. The brain's neural circuitry defines the mental switch period and determines its duration. This is similar to a computer screen's refresh rate. The brain's refresh rate seems to be 3 seconds long. Every 3 seconds our brain asks 'what is new?' and our sense of 'now' is updated.

Yet another clue for the duration of an experienced moment comes from the capacity of our short-term memory. Short-term memory is a mental system that stores temporary information for immediate use and manipulation. Our short-term memory capacity is defined as the amount of information we can hold in our minds without losing it in the presence of other information or distractions. Attempting to store more information above that capacity limit will result in losing the previous items. Now scientists have estimated that information is normally stored in short-term memory for about 2 to 5 seconds [8]. Afterwards, the information is either forgotten if you do not need it anymore, or is stored in our permanent long-term memory. Of course, this varies from one person to another. Some people have the ability to hold several items in their short-term memory while solving a problem or performing a distracting task and some can barely remember a sequence of three numbers. The capacity of our short-term memory determines our overall span of attention, which in turn sets a limit on the duration of our experienced moment that make up the present 'now'.

In a seminal paper, the eminent French experimental psychologist Paul Fraisse summarized the experimental findings of the last few decades and concluded that the present 'experienced moment' is a duration that can hardly extend beyond 5 seconds and has an average value of 2 to 3 seconds [8]. Three seconds is the length of time that an average person can keep something in his mind before having to store it in his long-term memory. If someone verbally told you his 10-digit phone number and asked you to dial it, you would most likely be able to do that if you manage to do it within 3 seconds. Of course, if you manage to devise a way that commits it to your long-term memory, then you do not need to worry about that time limit. Likewise, if you clap your hands three times, with about one second between each clap, when the third clap takes place, are you still *directly* aware of the first? Most likely not. That first clap will feel that it is already in the past and not part of the present 'now'. If, on the other hand, your claps were half a second apart, all three claps would feel as part of one present moment. As soon as their total duration exceeds 3 seconds, the first clap will be perceived as part of the past. Further evidence comes from sensorimotor control. In a typical experiment, a person is requested to synchronize a regular sequence of sound beeps with his finger taps. This kind of sensorimotor synchronization can only be reasonably accurate when the sound beeps are not more than 2 to 3 seconds apart. If the next sound beep lies too far in the future, say 5 seconds, it would not be possible to anticipate the finger taps accurately [9]. Three seconds is just about the longest time interval that we can perceive as 'now'.

It is therefore not by chance that the 3-second interval happens to show up in many areas of our lives. In songs and classical music, musical phrases blend nicely when they are made of musical motifs that are around 2 to 3 seconds long. The famous musical motif in Beethoven's 5th Symphony, the one that sounds like fate is knocking on your door, is around 3 seconds long. The same is true for poetry: the average duration of a spoken verse in most languages corresponds to about 3 seconds. This seems to be a universal phenomenon. Try that with any of Shakespeare's famous sonnets, 'Shall I compare thee to a summer's day?" Time yourself as you read it aloud and you will find it takes around 3 seconds. Radio stations use 3-second stings as breaks in a radio program. The soothing sound you hear at the startup of a Windows or Apple computer is 3 seconds long. Relaxation breathing takes about 3 seconds. In most cultures, a handshake lasts about 3 seconds. A hug also lasts for around the same duration. Psychologist Dr. Emese Nagy measured the duration of hugs while watching the Beijing Summer Olympics on television. Using video recordings of the event, she analyzed the duration of hugs between athletes from 32 nations in 21 sports. Whether it was with a coach, teammate, or rival, and regardless of gender, the hugs lasted on average about 3 seconds [10]. Similar cross-cultural studies have also shown that goodbye waves also last on average about 3 seconds. We seem to go through life experiencing the present in a series of 3-second windows. This time interval forms a basic temporal unit of consciousness that defines our perception of the present. This perception consists of a succession of brief 'experienced moments', an endless stream of 'nows', each lasting about 3 seconds on average, that roll on relentlessly as they bind the past with the future. And this brings us to the next point. How do we think about the past and future?

'We seem to go through life experiencing the present in a series of 3-second windows'

Space and Time: Perceiving the Past and Future

Our awareness of time in the past and future starts early on in life and comes in two forms; as a cycle and as a line. As we grow up we slowly develop consciousness of the world in the cyclic pace of seconds, minutes, hours, days and years. The school bell rings every hour, supper is served every evening, sunrises and sunsets recur each day, the seasons take turns every few months, birthdays repeat every year. Time is perceived as a set of cycles which form the basis of our ability to predict the future. Yet we also know that time is linear; it starts with a beginning in birth and an ending in death. In our mind, we place important events in our life on a timeline. If you speak a language that is written from left to right, such as English or French, you will tend to think of the past as something to the left while the future is something to the right. Most English speakers plot timelines from left to right. On the other hand, people whose native languages are Arabic or Hebrew, plot timelines the other way round. Because these languages are written from right to left, they tend to think of the past as something on the right and the future as something on the left. As we shall see shortly, Mandarin is written vertically, which explains why Chinese think of the future as something that is below! Interestingly, bilingual people tend to place the past and future in either position depending on what dominant language is used in formulating their thoughts.

Our sense of time is a fabrication of our brain to make sense of the events happening in our world. Since it is not a material object of the world, our brains cannot comprehend time without using physical notions such as distance and space. In English, for example, we talk about things taking a 'long' time, like a 'long' vacation or a 'short' movie. We say Christmas is fast 'approaching', the deadline is 'near', or the weekend is still 'far' off. We are looking 'forward' to meet someone or putting the past 'behind' us. We cannot think of time without thinking of space and distance, which is a further indication that time itself is not a property of the empirical world.

One significant aspect of this space-time relationship is the fact that our brains perceive the 'motion' of temporal events in the same way as it perceives the motion of physical objects. Any physical object can be easily identified within a certain space, but time is more abstract and needs to be imagined using space concepts. Consider, for example, these two sentences: (a) I moved my car forward two meters or (b) I moved the 3:00 p.m. meeting forward two hours. The car in the first sentence is a physical object that can travel through space and whose motion we can easily perceive. By contrast, there is no way we can experience the meeting's 'motion' through time using our senses. We just have to imagine it 'moving forward' in an abstract way. For some of us, this means the meeting is now at 5:00 p.m., while for others the meeting is now at 1:00 p.m. Both are equally correct and valid interpretations. It all depends on how you look at yourself in relation to time, or your 'time perspective'. You could see yourself standing still while the future moves towards you like a flowing river, from the future to the past. This is known as the *time-moving metaphor*. Examples of that are 'the deadline is fast approaching', 'Christmas will soon be upon us', or 'I cannot wait for my birthday to arrive'. Alternatively, you could see yourself moving in a straight line towards the future, as if on a conveyor belt, through fixed time. This is known as the *ego-moving metaphor*. Examples of that might be 'We are approaching the end of the month', 'we are falling behind schedule' or 'we will soon reach the year end.' Since we naturally seek good things and avoid bad things, we have a tendency to adopt one of these time perspectives depending on whether the approaching future event is something pleasant that we are looking forward to (ego-moving) or something unpleasant that we are shying away from (time-moving metaphor). More on that in a later chapter, when we explore how we experience the future.

Half of the World Disappeared

Additional intriguing evidence for that mental space-time relationship comes from people who have trouble comprehending time because of certain head injuries that affect their understanding of space. One such condition is called Left Hemispatial Neglect (LHN), which causes people to ignore the left side of nearly everything. A number of strange symptoms can arise from such a condition. A man with LHN may only shave the right half of his face, and a woman may only apply make-up to her right side. The left side of things do not exist in their mind. Patients with LHN do not see much of their left surroundings. They often bump into walls to their left, or leave the left half of the food on their plate. To understand how space is connected with time, psychologist Lera Boroditsky of the University of California in San Diego led a study with LHN French patients. French is written from left to right so French people tend to put past events on the left and future events on the right of a timeline. A group of seven French patients with LHN and a group of seven healthy people were told the story of a fictitious 40-year old man named David. The story involved events that happened to David 10 years in the past, when he was 30 years old and other events that will happen to him 10 years into the future, when he will be 50 years old. They were then asked to remember as many events about David as they could and to specify whether they occurred in his past or future. The researchers found that, compared to healthy people, the patients with LHN had a lot of trouble remembering the events from the past, but could easily remember the events related to the future. The results indicated that in the same way that LHN affects the left side of the space around patients, it also affected the left side of their mental time chronology which is normally associated with the past [11]. If the same study was conducted with LHN patients whose native language was Arabic or Hebrew, it would follow that they would have problems recalling future events. When someone's internal understanding of space is damaged, the sequence of time events and their perception of the future and past is disrupted.

Another indication of how time, space, and language are interrelated comes from languages such as Chinese Mandarin. English is written horizontally from left to right, while Chinese Mandarin is traditionally written vertically from top to bottom. This is why English speakers primarily talk about time as if it were a horizontal line, while Chinese Mandarin speakers usually describe time as a vertical line. In English, we look *forward* to the good times *ahead* or think *back* to the struggles of the past and be grateful that they are *behind* us. In Mandarin, most of the words used to describe that same sentence are vertical in nature, i.e. related to up and down. If you were to show a group of Chinese people an array of horizontal objects and then ask them what comes earlier, March or April, they will respond slower than if they had just seen a stack of vertical objects [12]. The converse is true for English speakers. Their answer will be slower than normal if they have just seen a stack of vertical objects before the question is asked. When the brain is primed to think vertically, it will require more effort to focus on horizontal concepts such as time, which explains why the responses are slower. Spatial representations that depend on our culture and language are essential to the way we think about time.

Time Estimation: Prospective vs. Retrospective

One more thing to mention here is the way we estimate time intervals. Psychologists found that when people are engaged in an activity that distracts their attention from tracking the passage of time, and are later asked how long they thought that activity took, they will give a very different estimate than if they were intentionally aware of the passing time. As an example, let us say that you just finished watching an episode of your favorite TV show and was unaware of the passing time, you look back and try to judge how long it has been going. Your time estimate is *retrospective,* because you were unaware of the passing time and you judged the time interval after the fact, relying purely on your memory of what has already occurred. In contrast, imagine you are waiting in a train station for the next train to arrive. You know the train arrives in about 10 minutes, but without any wristwatch or any clocks on the wall you try to guess when those 10 minutes will be over. You are consciously aware of the passing time and your estimate of when that interval elapses depends more on the amount of attention you devote to track the present time, and not the memory of what has already occurred. Your time is estimate is *prospective,* and psychologists refer to this as the experience of '*time-in-passing'.* It is important to distinguish between these two types of time judgments because they rely on different brain mechanisms and, as we shall see in subsequent chapters, they produce various time distortions with conflicting time experiences.

Recap

In brief, time and space are intricately intertwined in our minds. Our concepts of space, distance, and motion shape the way we experience the receding past and approaching future. Keep that in mind because, as we shall see later, this relationship can explain many aspects of the psychological time distortions that we experience every day.

As for our experience of the present, we saw that the longest time interval that can be perceived by our brain and still be called 'now' is on average about 3 seconds long. To slow down time and make the most of it, our aim should be to make our 'now' moments last longer. This would be useful in moments of bliss that we wish to extend. In situations where we need time to pass faster, such as moments of pain, we need to make our 'now' moments shorter. The key question, therefore, is what factors can stretch or shrink a 'now' moment so we can control the perceived speed of time? To answer that, we need to understand what 'now' is made up of and the brain mechanism that sets its duration. We will then cover what factors affect those brain mechanisms and explore ways that can expand or shrink our present 'now'.

In the next chapter, we will briefly take a look at the rudimentary inner workings of our brain that will help us understand the basic brain mechanisms responsible for perceiving reality. In the chapter following that, we will see how the speed at which we perceive reality defines the speed of time in our mind. We will then look at how psychologists have used what they know about time perception to create a simple internal clock model that we can use to explain how fast we experience the passage of time. This will then conclude the first part of the book and lay the foundations for understanding the various factors that affect the perceived speed of time, which we will cover in the second part, and how best to manipulate those to our advantage. For now, let us continue our journey into the depths of our brains.

CHAPTER 2

HOW DO OUR BRAINS PERCEIVE REALITY?

THE NEUROSCIENCE OF TIME PERCEPTION

'All our knowledge begins with the senses, proceeds then
to the understanding, and ends with reason. There is
nothing higher than reason.'
— Emmanuel Kant

The Real Purpose of our Brain

If you look closely at yourself in a mirror, behind those great looks, lies the sophisticated world of the most complex organ ever to be produced in the history of this universe: the human brain. Weighing around 1.4 Kg, this is the control center that runs all your bodily operations needed to keep you alive. The brain is made up of around 100 billion neuron cells (give or take) and each neuron is connected to another 10,000 other neurons, with the total connection exceeding the number of stars in the Milky Way galaxy. That is how complex the brain is. But what is the purpose of such a complex organ?

From an evolutionary point of view, one of the main reasons for our brain is not to help us think, feel, or create nice art, but actually to control the movement of our body. According to neuroscientists, a brain is useless in an organism that does not move. Consider plants and trees. They do not have a brain because they do not need to move. The sea squirt is a good example; it starts its life as a small tadpole that has one eye, one tail, and a very primitive brain that guides its movement in water. In the second part of its life, it searches for a suitable piece of rock to attach to for the remainder of its life and never moves again. Once it stops moving, does it use that time to contemplate on the meaning of life? No, it eats its own brain for energy!

Our brains evolved over millions of years, perfecting the way we move, long before we started developing any of the more sophisticated functions of thinking and planning. But why is movement so important? Remember that we evolved in a ruthless environment: eat or be eaten. Our ancestors had to develop the ability to move in search of food while avoiding becoming food themselves to other predators. That is the reason why our brains are counter-intuitively located inside our head. It would have made more sense for nature to place the brain in the chest area for better protection, rather than attaching it to the rest of the body by such a weak slim stem as our neck. But the brain is best located in the head because the eyes, ears, and nose are also situated there. These three sensory organs are best positioned in the head where they get the best view and optimal orientation when looking, sniffing, or listening for desired targets. With their millions of receptors receiving signals, such as light, smells, and sound vibrations from far distances, the sensory organs transmit critical information to the brain through a sophisticated network of neurons. The closer the brain is to those sensory organs, the faster the transmission speed. The eyes, ears and nose are essentially just an extension of the brain. They provide an early warning system for locating potential prey and predators, giving the brain enough time to react with a suitable plan of action. This power of prediction is the engine driving the evolution of intelligence in all animal species, especially humans. But what does this have to do with time?

Time is nothing but the measure of change. Without change, time would not exist. The great physicist, John Wheeler says 'Time is what keeps everything from happening at once'. Understanding how our brains perceive our changing reality is vital to our understanding of time and how we experience it. As we shall see, the crucial need to track motion and change is what eventually produced our sense of time, as a measure of change.

We Do Not 'See' What is Real

One aspect of the way we perceive reality is the fact that we only experience a partial image of reality that is filtered by our primary senses. Our senses of vision, hearing, smell, taste and touch provide the brain with signals that are used to paint a picture of reality that differs from the real world out there. For instance, red light has a wavelength of around 650 nanometers that is constant regardless of the observer. But what you see as 'red' is purely subjective and might be different from my perception of 'red', depending on how each brain processes that color wavelength. We could both look at a red apple and see it as 'red' but experience that 'red' color differently. There is no way to tell if your red is the same as mine, even though it is the same light wave that is being reflected off that apple. In fact, color does not really exist in the real world in the same way that material objects exist, but is a figment of our brain created from signals that are filtered by our unique senses. In the same way, we can all agree that chocolate tastes good, but there is no way for someone to know exactly how chocolate tastes to *you*. We do not see and taste what is real; only what we 'think' is real. There is an important distinction between the world as it is and the world as we perceive it, and we can never truly have access to the former, as the philosopher Emmanuel Kant duly observed. If you have seen *The Matrix* movie, you will recall a central question being raised on what is real and how do we define reality. The reality that we feel, smell, taste and see is simply electrical signals created and interpreted by our brains, even though they produce an image in our mind that is spectacular in its beauty and splendor.

How Our Brains Lag Behind Reality

In addition to the fact that we do not perceive true reality due to our brain's filtering mechanism, we also lag in time behind reality. The senses gather information from the outside world and send it to specific designated areas in the brain for processing. The brain's processing speed can be defined as the time it takes the brain to receive information, process it, and give an appropriate response. When you detect the smell of baking cookies, see the color of a flower, or hear the ringing of an alarm clock, it takes a fraction of a second for your brain to recognize that signal, identify a possible source, and respond. That fraction of a second is your reaction time. Psychologists use reaction time tests as a window to study how alert the brain is and how fast is its processing capabilities. They found that it takes about one tenth of a second for signals to reach the brain, even under conditions of most concentrated attention. This means that, for example, if you have to suddenly step on the car brakes because of an obstacle that appears in front of you, there will always be a time lag of at least one tenth of a second between when the obstacle appears and when your brain processes the information and decides on a response.

The notion that signals take time to travel to the brain came as a surprise in the 19th century as it was in conflict with the popular idea that the world is experienced instantaneously as it happened, i.e. without any lag between sensation and awareness. In 1850, German physiologist Hermann von Helmholtz experimented with frogs by connecting their leg muscles with wire so that when the muscle contracted it switched on a lamp in a circuit. By showing the frog scary images that caused its legs to contract, he found that it took about a tenth of a second (or 100 milliseconds) for a signal to travel from the brain to the muscle and cause the lamp to switch on. In another experiment, Helmholtz applied mild electric shocks to people's skin and asked them to give a sign as soon as they felt it. In spite of the participants' dismay, his results confirmed that sensory signals took time to travel to the brain. In fact, people took longer to respond to shocks that were applied to the toe because the path to the brain was longer when compared to shocks applied to the lower back.

Of our five senses, vision is responsible for the largest portion of information processed by the brain. It is certainly our most dominant sense.

Hearing complements vision even though each perceives the world in a different way. When you hear a car honk, you can find out which car made the sound by detecting the direction the sound came from and by looking at the car closest to it. Our brain integrates both to perceive reality in a seamless way. The speeds at which these signals travel to the brain vary from one sense to another. To appreciate the complex challenge that the brain faces, all sensory signals arrive at different brain areas at slightly different times and are processed at different speeds. The color, motion, and sound signals of a red Ferrari that is zooming past you at high speed are all combined into a single perception in your mind, even though the processing of these sensory signals is distributed over several brain locations. The brain's auditory cortex, for instance, processes an audio signal from your ear faster than a visual signal is processed in the visual cortex. The difference is around 40 milliseconds, which is not much, but enough to justify using a gun for starting a race, instead of a light flash. The faster audio processing speed means that sprint runners react more quickly to a bang than to a flash of light. This incidentally is another vestige of evolution that we inherited from our days in the jungle, when we could hear a tiger long before we could see it!

The brain must account for the discrepancies in the signals' travel time and processing speeds, yet still manages to synchronize all incoming signals and construct a unified perception of the world that is extremely precise. An example of this synchronization was discovered when people started watching TV in the 1960s. In the early days of television broadcasting, engineers found it problematic to keep audio and video signals synchronized. They then accidentally discovered that as long as the signals arrived within one tenth of a second, or 100 milliseconds of each other, the viewers' brains would automatically synchronize the signals and not notice the lag. If the time difference between receiving the audio and video signals were more than 100 milliseconds, the broadcast would start to appear like a poorly dubbed Chinese Kung Fu movie. The reason was revealed when neuroscientists found a 100 milliseconds delay from the moment you sense something to the moment it is registered in your brain. The brain needs that split of a second to integrate the various information arriving from all senses and tag them as one event. To do that, the brain has to wait for the slowest sensory signal to catch up with the fastest, so that it sends them off all at once. What you are seeing right now on this page is actually a delayed live broadcast! Your eyes have sensed it 100 milliseconds ago. It is as if you are constantly living in the past, like a radio station that broadcasts with a five-second delay, to avoid bloopers. You might say 100 milliseconds are not much really. Negligible, right? Well, apparently not.

Using the brain's ability to synchronize and integrate the timing of various sensory signals, scientists can play weird tricks with the brain, even creating the feeling that time is going backwards! In 2006, American neuroscientist Dr. David Eagleman, and his collaborators, came up with a fascinating experiment to investigate how this affects our sense of causality [13]. Volunteers were allowed to play a computer game in which a light flashed when they clicked the mouse button. Unknown to the participants, the experimenters introduced a fixed delay of 150 milliseconds between the mouse click and the light flash. However, after a few tries, the participants playing the game quickly adapted to the delay and felt as though the flash appeared immediately after the mouse click. Their brains automatically adjusted for that delay, subconsciously cutting it out completely, in the same way that viewers of early TV broadcasts automatically synchronized the timing lag between audio and video signals. Now, the fascinating discovery was that when the experimenters later removed the delay, the volunteers started seeing the flash before they even pressed the button! What had happened was that the brain was tricked and started switching the order of events so that they were seeing the outcome before the action. Cause and effect were reversed. It was as if time was going backwards!

Neurotransmitters: The Brain's Messengers

The synchronization and processing of sensory signals arriving from the various senses occurs in a fraction of a second. The speed of processing this information depends on how fast the brain neurons can talk to each other, which in turn depends on the level of brain chemicals called 'neurotransmitters'. All of our thoughts, emotions, and actions rely on these chemical messengers and their role in allowing neurons to communicate. When a neuron wants to transmit an electric signal to the next neuron, it releases a neurotransmitter into the space between them. The neurotransmitter binds to a receptor on the other side, which then transmits the signal to the adjacent neuron. The adjacent neuron then repeats the same sequence, and so on so forth (several hundred times per second). Neurons fire, reset, and fire again at phenomenal speeds, such that if you were to stretch a series of neurons across a football field, an electric signal could traverse the full length in just one second!

Neuroscientists have so far discovered over 50 neurotransmitters in the brain and identified which ones are responsible for processing information. They found that neurotransmitters, such as dopamine, play an important role in time perception. Time is a measure of change and the perceived speed of time is a measure of how fast we perceive change. This in turn depends on how fast the brain can process the ever changing sensations detected by our senses. The brains information processing speed relies heavily on the amount of neurotransmitters that are available in the brain for communication. Neuroscientists also found that abnormal levels of these brain chemicals are behind most mental disorders like Schizophrenia, Parkinson's disease, ADHD, mania, or depression and, in some cases, the drivers of creativity and genius thinking. A simple analogy to illustrate this is taking your car for a regular maintenance service. The car operates using a variety of fluids such as engine oil, brake fluid, anti-freeze coolant and transmission oil. The car needs to have all fluid levels within the normal range to work properly. In the same way, too much or too little of these brain neurotransmitters will affect the various brain functions like alertness, attention, and information processing speed. But what is relevant to our subject, is the fact that the level of these neurotransmitters in the brain play an important role in how fast we experience the subjective flow of time. As we shall see in chapter 8, this is confirmed by studies that have shown how people with abnormal levels of neurotransmitters and suffering from ADHD, Parkinson's, Alzheimer, Schizophrenia or depression, all experience a different speed of time.

The infinitesimal time it takes for our brain to process sensory information determines how fast we can absorb the ever-changing reality around us. As we shall see later, this brain processing speed, in turn, affects how fast we experience time. Therefore, it is important to understand the brain mechanisms that are behind this processing speed and how scientists measure it.

Brainwaves: The Brain's Electricity

When groups of neurons release brain neurotransmitters to communicate and process sensory information, they generate spikes of electrical activity inside the brain. This was first observed in 1875 by British electro-physiologist Richard Caton when he introduced an electrode in a monkey's brain and laid the groundwork for the discovery of brainwaves. Following that discovery, German Psychiatrist Hans Berger invented in 1924 the EEG (Electroencephalography) for recording brain electrical activity and brainwaves. The story goes that Hans was in military service when he fell from his horse and landed in the path of a horse-drawn cannon. Luckily, the driver halted the horses in time leaving Hans shaken but with no serious injuries. At the same time, his sister who was at home many miles away had a feeling he was in danger and sent him a telegram. That incident made such an impression on Hans that he believed his thoughts about his imminent death must have been somehow transmitted miles away to his close sister. His belief made him determined to find out how the brain transmits 'psychic energy' and eventually led to the invention of EEG for recording electrical activity in the human brain.

The EEG records the synchronized electrical pulses from the billions of neurons in the form of brainwaves. The number and magnitude of the electrical spikes produced depends on the task we are doing, such as active thinking, dreaming, sleeping, or meditating. It defines how alert we are. When sleeping, fewer neurons are active and so brainwaves are slow with high amplitudes. In activities like reading or calculating, more neurons are active and brainwaves are fast with lower amplitudes. The higher the intensity and speed at which our neurons are firing, the faster our EEG brainwaves, the more alert we will be, and of course, the faster we can process sensory information. As we shall see, this in turn, is crucial to how fast we experience the speed of time. Scientists use brainwave recordings to assess the brain's overall information processing speed. The faster you can react to a stimulus, the more intense is the required electrical activity going on inside your brain. Consequently, people with faster brainwaves have faster reaction times and faster information processing speeds compared to people with slower brainwaves [14, 15]. They are also generally quick thinkers, impulsive, hyper-sensitive, emotional, and highly stimulated compared to those with slower brainwaves who are described as calm, cautious, steady, and slow.

'The higher the intensity and speed at which our neurons are firing, the faster our EEG brainwaves, the more alert we will be, and the faster we can process sensory information'

Brainwaves and the level of electrical activity inside the brain are also important to what psychologists call 'psychomotor speed'. It simply means being able to coordinate thinking fast with doing something fast, like driving a car. While driving you are constantly looking around, watching other cars and monitoring what your car is doing in relation to other cars, the pedestrians, and that cat attempting to commit suicide by crossing the road. At the same time, you are pressing the brake or accelerator and turning the steering wheel to navigate to your destination. Your brain does all that on autopilot in a smooth, subconscious way. Psychomotor speed is also important in our ability to understand conversations. When you are listening to what someone is saying, you are taking in all sorts of sounds, making sense of that noise, and figuring out the meaning before you receive the next stream of sound bites. In older people, a slower psychomotor speed makes it harder for them to understand and follow conversations. That is because psychomotor speed depends on the overall collective action of brain neurons, which tends to decline with age.

The brainwaves therefore act as a sort of an 'internal clock' or timer that regulates the pace at which sensory information is processed. As we shall see in a subsequent chapter, the level of innate electrical activity and brainwaves also help define certain traits of our personality, such as being an introvert or extrovert, patient or impulsive, a morning or a night person, and how easily we get bored. These traits affect the speed at which we experience time as well.

Recap

To sum up what we have covered so far, our brain is in the business of detecting motion and controlling our body's movement by capturing sensory information and processing this in a specific order so that the world makes sense to us. The processing of this sensory information takes a fraction of a second which is why we are always lagging slightly behind reality. The brain's electrical activity and level of neurotransmitters determine the speed at which our brain absorbs and processes sensory information. This brain information processing speed can be assessed by measuring reaction times and performing psychomotor speed tests. It can also be measured by the amount of electrical activity produced by neurons that is displayed as brainwaves in EEG scans. This electrical activity reflects the state of our brain's consciousness and alertness, from fully awake to drowsy and fully asleep, and as we shall see next, it defines the essence of our time experience. With this basic understanding of the inner workings of our brain, we are now ready to look at how our ability to detect the ever-changing world around us defines our sense of time. You will have to bear with me a slightly longer chapter next, but I promise it is worth the effort.

CHAPTER 3

TIME – THE ULTIMATE ILLUSION

HOW DO OUR BRAINS PROCESS TIME?

'For us believing physicists the distinction between past,
present and future is only an illusion, if a stubborn one'
— Albert Einstein

Our Brain's Video Camera

To our mind, the world appears to be smooth and continuous. When we say that the world is continuous, we mean that it is persistently active and undergoing continuous change as time goes on. However, neuroscientists have accumulated a sizeable amount of evidence indicating that the way we perceive reality and process sensory information is not continuous but actually discrete. In other words, it seems that our brains do not process reality as a continuous stream but rather in discrete chunks, or mental snapshots, each having a short duration, similar to how a video camera records a sequence of still snapshots on film. When you observe a fast moving car, you might see it moving in a smooth continuous way, but recent evidence shows that this is illusive! Our experience of the world only appears continuous in the same way that a movie appears continuous even though it is made up of discrete motionless images that are replayed at a fast speed to give the illusion of continuous motion. As we shall shortly see, the speed at which we experience the flow of time has much to do with the speed at which these mental snapshots flow inside our brain.

Buddhists' holy texts were among the earliest sources to propose that consciousness is not continuous but consists of a sequence of extremely fast discrete events referred to as 'momentary collections of mental phenomena' or 'distinct moments'. Numerous philosophers also put forward similar notions in the 18th century, such as David Hume who noted that the stream of our thoughts is 'nothing but a bundle or collection of different perceptions, which succeed each other with an inconceivable rapidity. The mind is a kind of theatre, where several perceptions successively make their appearance.' [16] The speed of thought is the speed at which these perceptions are processed in the brain. This is known as the discrete perception hypothesis, or mental snapshot hypothesis. It was neglected after having fallen out of favor over the past 50 years because a substantial portion of the evidence up to that point, although provocative, was not definitive. However, in recent years, and with accumulating experimental data, the theory found renewed fervor and has regained support. We will explore some of that evidence shortly, but the whole idea is based on the fact that the brain, like a video camera, seems to record reality in small discrete mental snapshots, at a recording speed of several snapshots per second, and weaves them together to give the illusion of continuous seamless motion [17]. According to Francis Crick, Nobel Prize winner, biophysicist, and co-discoverer of the DNA molecule structure, consciousness not only comes in discrete mental snapshots, but the experience of motion is itself illusory; "perception might well take place in discrete processing epochs, perceptual moments, or snapshots. Your subjective life could be a ceaseless sequence of such snapshots." In that sense, life is a movie, your eyes are the camera lens, and your brain is the video camera!

The Speed of Time

Since it is impossible to conceive of time without change, it is reasonable to expect a relationship between our time experience and the way we perceive change. The speed of time that we experience has to do with the speed at which we perceive change. The best way to illustrate that relationship is by using the video camera analogy. If you own one of the latest iPhone or Android smartphones, you might have noticed a video recording feature called 'Slo-Mo' mode. It is normally used to capture fast action sports or racing scenes and renders them in slow motion. In the normal video mode, a scene is usually recorded at a speed of 30 frames per second (fps) but with the Slo-Mo mode, the latest models now boast cameras that are fast enough to capture videos at a recording speed of 240 fps. If you switch your smartphone to that high speed recording mode and capture a fast action scene at 240 fps, you will notice that when the scene is later replayed at the normal speed of 30 fps, it will appear in slow motion, exactly as if time had slowed down. The reason for that slow motion effect is that, when filming at 240 fps, every second will contain 240 frames which will be spread over 8 seconds when they replayed at the normal speed of 30 fps. Therefore, every second that is captured at the fast recording speed will appear 8 times longer and time will seem to be running slowly.

This is somehow similar to what goes on inside our brains, but of course to a much lesser extent. Let us assume that we perceive the world at an average speed of 10 mental snapshots per second. Every time our brain captures 10 snapshots, it assumes that one second has elapsed. Now imagine that your brain's processing speed is suddenly given a boost, say from a dose of drug stimulants such as LSD or amphetamine drugs (speed), which causes a surge in brain electrical activity and allows the brain to start capturing 20 snapshots per second. Under normal circumstances, 20 snapshots would have taken two seconds to record at the brain's normal recording speed of 10 fps. When those 20 snapshots are processed, the brain assumes that they must have spanned a period of two seconds instead of the one 'real' second that was actually needed to record them. One second of 'real' time will contain 2-seconds worth of information and will therefore appear to have stretched, as if time had passed slowly. Such experiences, as we shall see later in more detail, have been confirmed by people who take drugs that stimulate the brain. The faster our brain is at processing sensory information, the faster mental snapshots flow in our mind, and the slower time appears to run. The speed at which we experience the flow of time is nothing but the speed of our thoughts.

The converse can also explain how time seems to fly in certain situations. In the 1920s, when movie making was still in its early days, silent films were recorded at a slow speed of 16 frames per second and had to be replayed at much higher frame rates to look continuous and real. This made the movie appear as if it was running in fast-forward mode. Charlie Chaplin style movies are a perfect case in point; everything moves literally faster than normal as if time was running fast. This analogy helps us understand what goes on in the brain when it records fewer mental snapshots per second, say 5 fps instead of the normal 10 fps, for the sake of demonstration. This means it will need two seconds to capture the 10 snapshots it normally captures in one second. When those 10 snapshots are processed, the brain assumes that the two seconds it took to capture them is just one second. At that rate, two minutes will seem like just one minute and the day will be over before you know it. The slower your brain is in processing sensory information, the faster time seems to run. This seemingly inverse relationship is important to understand why we sometimes experience time as speeding up or slowing down. So how fast are we actually processing reality?

'The slower your brain is at processing sensory information, the faster time seems to run, and vice versa'

How Long is a Mental Snapshot?

The brain's processing speed is directly linked to the duration of our mental snapshots. The shorter the snapshots, the faster is information being processed. One clue for the duration of a mental snapshot comes from what psychologists call the Phi phenomenon, also known as 'apparent motion'. A simple example will illustrate. Suppose two circles are flashed successively at two separate locations on a computer screen. If the time interval between them is short enough, we will not be able to distinguish them successively, and the circles will appear simultaneously. As we saw earlier, this has to do with the time needed for sensory signals to register in our brain. However, if the interval is increased to at least 50 milliseconds, or 20 flashes per second, something quite dramatic occurs; one of the circles will appear to move smoothly to the other circle in an alternating back and forth motion, despite the fact that the circles are really just flashing on and off at their fixed locations. The perceived motion of the circle is entirely supplied by our brain which is happy to fill in the blanks. This is very fortunate for movie lovers, since this phenomenon is not just confined to flashing circles but extends to complex sequence of still images that make up a movie. This phenomenon gives a clue on how the brain manages to perceive continuous motion from a sequence of mental snapshots.

In movies, the faster the recording speed, the closer the motion on film is to reality. Modern VHS and digital video recording technologies usually record movies at 24 frames per second (fps). TVs operate at 30 fps and computer monitors at 60 fps. Actually anything above 10 fps, i.e. one frame every 100 milliseconds, will give the illusion of smooth continuous motion. When The Hobbit movie was released at a frame rate of 48 fps, it caused uproar in the movie industry and among some moviegoers who found it too real! Replay that movie at a speed of less than 10 fps and motion will appear jerky. The movie will start to look like a quick slide show and the illusion of continuous motion disappears. This 10 fps critical recording speed implies that film snapshots should not be more than 100 milliseconds apart for our brains to perceive a sense of continuity in motion. But what is so special about that short time interval of 100 milliseconds?

In 1860, the biologist Karl Ernst von Baer gave an important lecture to the Russian Academy of Sciences in St. Petersburg where he introduced the notion of a 'life moment' being the shortest time interval that can be perceived by a living being [18]. Von Baer suspected that different animal species, having different brain sizes and sensory organs, most likely had different durations for their 'life moments'. This meant that they experienced the flow of time at different speeds. For von Baer, the most important bodily process for time perception was the speed at which our sensory organs can detect new sensations. Based on early experiments, he speculated that humans could enjoy around 10 'life moments' or mental snapshots within one second (this would be less for other species, such as turtles or snails). From that, he concluded that the length of a human 'moment' is not more than 100 milliseconds, the same duration that creates the illusion of continuity in movies.

Time durations in the range of 100 milliseconds appear to form basic units of human consciousness and play an important role in how the brain operates. Take a small object, say a key, tie it to a string and twirl it rapidly. If it makes a full turn in less than a tenth of a second, or 100 milliseconds, it will seem as if it is equally spread out in a closed circle. When you slow down the rotating speed, you will start to see the key again distinctly and the closed circle disappears. Rotating the string at a speed of 10 turns per second gives the illusion of continuous motion, similar to the minimum recording speed needed to produce continuous motion on film. As Nobel Prize winner and physiologist, Charles Richet, wrote: "An elementary mental vibration has a certain duration, and that duration is approximately a tenth of a second." He believed that this duration was a measure of the speed of our thoughts. Another evidence comes from the average reading speed. Try to read as many words as you can in ten seconds and you will notice that, despite your best efforts, the number is about a hundred, one word every tenth of a second. One tenth of a second also appears to be the shortest time interval for taking an action and appears in many reaction time experiments as we saw earlier. The 100-millisecond time interval appears to be a fundamental feature of our brain's information processing speed.

Shortly after Von Baer's speculation, scientists started conducting all sorts of experiments to determine the duration of mental snapshots in order to determine how fast our brains 'record' reality. In 1903, Professor J.P. Hylan concluded from several experiments that when people are presented with 6 consecutive letters popping on a screen, they will appear simultaneous if they fall within an interval of approximately 80 milliseconds and can only be perceived distinctly if they are spread out over a longer interval of time [19]. In an effort to measure these mental snapshots or 'perceptual moments', psychologist G.A Brecher devised an ingenious set of experiments that established the minimum time required for the brain to distinctly perceive two or more events presented in sequence. His estimates were on average 57 milliseconds. Any two distinct events falling within that time interval would be perceived as simultaneous. Further research confirmed that sensory signals, whether visual, auditory, or touch, will only appear to be successive if they are separated by a minimum interval that ranges from 25 to 100 milliseconds. We, therefore, cannot detect more than 10 to 40 sensory stimulations per second, which is quite close to the 10 'life moments' that was estimated by Von Baer more than a hundred years earlier. In light of all that, psychologist J.M. Stroud introduced the notion of the 'discrete moment' or mental snapshot, and concluded from empirical evidence accumulated over the last few decades that, in order to be able to distinguish between two events, the time interval between them should be around 100 milliseconds long [20]. Each mental snapshot is associated with a mental impression of color, motion, sound and so on, captured from the senses.

Measuring Mental Snapshots with Flickering Lights

To measure the duration of our mental snapshots, scientists use flickering lights to assess the number of visual events that can be distinctly identified each second by our eyes. Imagine you are observing a flickering light source that is emitting, say, 5 flashes per second. You can easily see each individual flash clearly separated by fleeting instants of darkness. However, as you start to increase the rate of flicker, you will reach a frequency where the light flickers so fast that you can no longer distinguish the distinct flashes but you start seeing a steady or continuous light instead. That critical flickering speed is called the Flicker Fusion Frequency (FFF) and is a measure of our brain's 'recording' speed. At that flickering frequency, your brain can no longer perceive the instants of darkness separating the flashes as they fuse into a constant steady light.

Scientists have been measuring FFF values in humans for decades and have arrived at a range of 10 to 40 flashes per second (fps) [21]. Brain 'recording' speeds have also been found to vary among animal species.

Von Baer was right when he suggested, back in 1862, that different animals experience different flow of subjective time, depending on their size. Like humans, the speed at which animals perceive reality depends on how rapidly their nervous system can process sensory information. As explained above, this can be assessed by measuring the speed at which a fast-flickering light cannot be distinguished anymore and appears continuous. Generally, the smaller the animal and the faster its metabolic rate, the faster the flickering light it can detect, the faster information can be processed and the slower time passes. Have you ever wondered how birds manage to chase one another through a forest at lightning speeds without colliding with branches or ending up splattered against a tree? Animals smaller than us see the world in slow motion. That is how birds manage to avoid smashing into trees. Scientists, for instance, found that a pigeon's brain can record up to 100 frames per second (fps) and ground squirrels can grasp 120 fps [22]. A higher FFF gives animals an advantage when pursuing a fast-moving target. Pigeons rely on the high recording speed to flee from a predator, dive down to snatch prey, or zero in on a nest for precise landing. It allows them those few extra seconds to peck at seeds on the road and fly away at the last possible moment before a car approaches.

Dogs can also process visual information at least 25 percent faster than humans. If you own a dog, you may be surprised to know that when your pet is sitting next to you watching TV, it sees a flickering screen. That is because TVs flicker at 30 Hz but provide the illusion of continuous images because of our lower temporal resolution compared to the higher frequencies at which they operate. Dogs, however, can detect that flicker because their visual system has a higher refresh rate than that of TV screens. You might think they are enjoying the movie, but all they can see is constant flicker, they just enjoy your company! For them it would probably be more enjoyable if the movie was played on a computer monitor because of its higher flickering frequency (60 Hz). Similar studies on shark vision have revealed that they experience flicker fusion at about 45 fps, nearly twice the frequency at which humans cease to see distinct flashes. Chickens can perceive flickering at around 90 fps. This means they can easily detect the flickering of florescent lamps that are generally used to artificially illuminate poultry housing farms, creating unnecessary and constant stress for these poor animals.

The highest FFFs in animals belong to insects, like houseflies and honeybees, which can perceive motion at the colossal rate of up to 300 fps. This remarkable recording speed is what makes it so hard to hit a housefly with a rolled-up newspaper. The fly perceives the swift strike in 'bullet time', similar to a slow-motion action scene in movies like The Matrix. For a fly, time runs at least 20 times more slowly than it does for humans. This gives it ample time to escape and easily evade the strike in the same way that Keanu Reeves evades the bullets in that famous scene. Flies might not be deep thinkers, but they can make good decisions extremely quickly.

At the other end of the spectrum, lower Flicker Fusion Frequencies can be found in animal species that have a slower pace of life. The leatherback sea turtle, for instance, has an FFF of just 14 fps [22]. The lowest known FFF belongs to a deep-sea creature (the Booralana Tricarinata) which boasts only 4 fps. Its temporal resolution is so low that it is unlikely it could track any moving objects. For these species, life looks like one brief and boring slide show!

To recap, flicker fusion tests are used to measure the maximum number of visual snapshots our brain can perceive each second. They are used to assess the brain's processing speed and are good indicators of how fast we are 'recording' the world, hence how fast time is experienced. The average Flicker Fusion Frequency for humans is 10 to 40 fps. This means the time interval between flashes are in the range 25 to 100 milliseconds, the same range in which movie snapshots give the illusion of continuous motion. But what is it inside the brain that defines the duration of these mental snapshots? To be able to control the speed of time, we need to understand how our brain's 'video camera' produces those short-lived mental snapshots?

How Our Brains create Mental Snapshots

As we have seen, a key aspect of the discrete theory of perception is that elements of information received through the senses are perceived as distinct 'life moments' or mental snapshots. The external world is continuously changing and the brain needs to track these changes and update its consciousness to keep up with reality. Our senses of vision, hearing, and touch are constantly confronted with a continuous stream of sensory information. But the updating and processing of sensory information takes a tiny fraction of a second that depends on the firing speed of brain neurons and, in particular, the time needed to synchronize neuron assemblies. These neurons communicate with each other by releasing neurotransmitters (or electrical signals) in a discrete and non-continuous way, creating synchronized patterns of electrical spikes that we detect as brainwaves in EEG scans. Information, therefore, cannot be processed in an equally continuous manner at each moment in time, but is captured and processed in discrete chunks, or 'mental snapshots.' The 'recording' process leaves a signature, at the neuron level, in the form of electrical spikes that rise and fall in intensity with every captured mental snapshot. By measuring the timing of these EEG electrical spikes (brainwaves), we can assess the speed at which our brain's 'video camera' updates our consciousness and the number of mental snapshots it records each second. The discrete nature of this process also implies that distinct events that occur within the confines of one mental snapshot are blended to produce one single and continuous experience. Let us look at an example to clarify this.

As I sit in the park, I see a youngster riding his skateboard, moving in a continuous straight line down the track. By continuous, I mean that the skateboard does not disappear here and reappear there but successively occupies every point along its path, at every point in time. Now if I take a video camera and start filming the teenager on his skateboard, his continuous motion will be recorded in a discontinuous and discrete manner on film in the form of a rapid sequence of snapshots. When I replay the film, the recorded skateboard snapshots do not really move at all; they are just replayed at such a fast rate giving the skateboard the illusion of continuous real-life motion. The recording speed of a typical video camera is 24 snapshots per second. Consequently, the duration of each film snapshot is 42 milliseconds long. The video camera does not record every instant of time but snaps a sample of reality every 42 milliseconds. Any events happening in between those film snapshots would not be recorded as distinct events but would fuse into one of the snapshots on film. If an alien spaceship, for instance, appears out of nowhere and pulls the boy 20 meters in the air after one snapshot is taken and then puts him back to exactly where he was and vanishes, before the next snapshot is taken, the video camera would not capture that. That single snapshot taken by the video camera before the highly unlikely event represents all positions occupied by the skateboard during the 42-millisecond window. Within that film 'moment', reality is simply not processed by the video camera and, therefore, slips by unrecorded, as if time froze.

Our brains work in a similar discrete way, and thus the events falling between two mental snapshots cannot be detected by our brains, but would fuse and be recorded as one snapshot in our mind. To investigate that, an intriguing study was conducted in 2010 at the Brain and Cognition Research Centre in Toulouse, France, where participants were presented with very brief flashes of light on a computer screen while they were connected to an EEG scanning machine that recorded their brain's electrical activity. After each light flash, a question mark appeared on the screen and the participant had to press a button to indicate if he or she saw the flash or not. Each participant performed 1,500 trials and the results indicated that on average only half of the flashes were detected. This raised the question as to what was causing the other half to be entirely missed. We saw that the brain's electrical activity comes and goes in waves, or spikes, cycling rapidly between phases of high and low electrical activity states. Researchers suspected that mental snapshots were being captured at the high activity states, while the low activity states were those moments in between snapshots. When they compared the EEG brainwave recordings with the flash detection results, they found that the probability to detect a light flash strongly depended on the phase of the brainwave cycles that shortly preceded the presentation of the flash. Participants who were presented with a flash that coincided with a spike in their brainwave (positive phase) were more likely to detect it, whereas a flash could not be easily perceived when it coincided with a drop in the brainwave (negative phase) [23, 24]. This suggests that our perception operates in successive periodic cycles that rapidly alternate between favorable periods with high spikes in electrical activity, where we consciously detect lights flashes, and unfavorable periods with drops in electrical activity, where we miss them.

The reason for this is that neurons are more likely to fire and detect a light flash when they are already in the excited positive phase of the brainwave cycle and less likely to fire when they are in the inhibited negative phase. In other words, a mental snapshot is only recorded in our mind around the peak of each brainwave cycle [25]. These brainwave cycles act like a fast camera shutter that cuts the continuous visual sequence into discrete mental snapshots.

Brainwaves come in various types and speeds, the most dominant being the Alpha brainwaves that occurs when the brain is resting or in quiet flowing thought. They have an average frequency of 10 Hz, i.e. one spike every 100 milliseconds. Therefore, when we are resting, our brains will perceive reality at the rate of 10 snapshots per second or one snapshot every 100 milliseconds. When the brain is more alert such as when solving problems, planning, or critical thinking, brainwaves run up to around 40 Hz and a higher number of mental snapshots are captured. The slowest brainwaves occur during deep meditation or dreamless sleep, when we are less alert and very few mental snapshots are processed.

The Wagon Wheel Illusion

Further evidence for the discrete perception of reality comes from the so-called wagon wheel illusion. You might have noticed that in fast action movies, the wheels of a car seem to be rotating backwards when the vehicle is clearly moving forward. This is obvious in racing scenes or speeding stagecoaches in Western movies. The illusion occurs because the recording speed at which the movie is filmed, usually 24 frames per second, is slower than the speed at which the wheels are turning. The result is that the video camera captures one discrete snapshot of the rotating wheel at a position that moves slightly behind with every turn. When these positions are replayed in film, the wheel appears to be rotating backwards giving rise to the illusion. In engineering terms, this process is called 'aliasing'. Surprisingly, this wagon wheel illusion is not just limited to movie scenes but can also be observed in real life under continuous light. You can actually notice it when looking intently at the wheels of a car traveling on the highway lane beside you, in jet fan engines, cooling fan blades, or in airplane propellers rotating in broad daylight. This implies that internal 'aliasing' is also taking place within the visual system itself and our brains must be working like a video camera. Our brain's visual system appears to be sampling the motion of the turning wheel periodically, in a series of discrete snapshots, that causes the wheel to be perceived as rotating backwards [26].

The first to observe the wagon-wheel effect under truly continuous light was J.F Schouten, a Dutch physicist, in 1967. He noticed that the spokes on a wheel that is rotating at a rate of 8 – 12 cycles per second (Hz) can be seen as standing still under focused attention and would appear in reverse rotation when the wheel turns at a faster speed of 30 -35 cycles per second. He, however, interpreted these observations by suggesting that the rotating wheel is processed not only by visual detectors sensitive to the true rotation but also by detectors sensitive to the reverse rotation. The illusion appears in a form of rivalry between the reverse direction detectors that become sufficiently active to dominate perception of the true rotation detectors [27]. This interpretation opposes the discrete perception theory and a debate in the scientific community has been going on as to which of the two interpretations is closer to the truth. There is strong evidence that supports each side but the balance seems to be tipping recently towards the discrete perception theory.

Further research confirmed that the continuous wagon wheel illusion is most prominent when the rotation speed is in the range of 10 to 16 Hz and is greatest around 13 Hz (rotating 13 times per second). Interestingly, if you observe the illusion while connected to an EEG machine, there is only one frequency band in your EEG brainwaves that changes significantly when you see the illusion, and that is the 13 Hz brainwave, the same frequency of the rotating wheel. This coincides with the range of alpha brainwaves (8 to 13 Hz) and implies that the visual part of the brain 'records' around 13 snapshots per second, or one snapshot every 77 milliseconds when the illusion is observed [28, 29]. This provides further evidence that the speed of the neurons' cyclic firing pattern is why we observe reverse motion in the wagon wheel illusion and why the brain absorbs reality in a discrete and discontinuous manner.

The wagon wheel experiments illusion depend on the degree of focused attention one devotes to observing the rotating wheel [30]. When two rotating wheels are viewed simultaneously, the reverse motion is only observed in one wheel at a time, as if attention flips successively between the two wheels allowing the illusion to be only observed in one wheel at a time. This raises the question as to whether the way we pay attention is a discrete cyclic process or whether it is a continuous one.

Our Attention: Blinking or Continuous?

The consensus for the past 30 years was that attention works like the scanning beam of a searchlight that lights up parts of the vision field and analyzes successive targets that come into focus. However, there is now increasing evidence suggesting that our attention can concurrently select multiple locations or targets. But what is uncertain is whether that ability relies on a continuous allocation of attention to all targets at the same time- the 'parallel strategy'- or whether attention switches rapidly between targets in a discrete and sequential manner, known as the 'sampling strategy'. A simple example will illustrate. Imagine you are meeting a friend in a crowded coffee shop. You arrive late and start scanning the room in search of your friend. Do you move your eyes from face to face like a roaming spotlight, or do you take in the whole scene hoping that your friend's face pops out at you? Researchers at MIT found that people tend to scan the room, switching from face to face, in a discrete sequential manner. But what determines how fast you can scan the room? The timing of each switch in attention appears to be regulated by the level of electrical activity in the brain that acts like an internal built-in clock, providing the framework for shifting attention from one target to the next in a sequential manner [31, 32]. Several studies have confirmed that attention seems to work like a nightclub's flashing stroboscope or a blinking spotlight that scans targets at an intrinsic rate of 7 items per second. That is one switch every 140 milliseconds. This again coincides with the range of our mental snapshot durations that we saw earlier [33].

Attention is considered the gateway to our consciousness. Thus, if the attention gateway of our mind opens and closes in a fast periodic manner, at the rate of 7 times per second, then the contents of our awareness will also be rapidly updated at the same rate and in a discrete periodic manner. Our brain's electrical fluctuations and brainwaves define the speed of that periodic updating and define the duration of the successive mental snapshots of our awareness. Faster information processing, means more mental snapshots are being captured within a certain time interval, causing that interval to stretch in our mind, as if time ran slowly, and vice versa. So what have we learned so far?

Recap

Even though the world appears to be continuous, the brain does not process sensory information in a continuous manner. It absorbs reality in discrete chunks, in a sequence of rapid mental snapshots, similar to a video camera. The brain mechanism behind this discrete perception has to do with our brainwaves, i.e. the periodic fluctuations of electrical spikes that rise and fall in intensity with every recorded snapshot. Our brainwaves play a major role in chunking the continuous visual stream into discrete mental snapshots that span intervals of 25 to 100 milliseconds long, or the equivalent recording speed of 10 to 40 snapshots per second. These brainwaves, having a similar range of 10 Hz to 40 Hz, regulate the speed of our thoughts, the speed at which we absorb reality from all around us, and the duration of our mental snapshots.

The perceived speed of time is a reflection of the speed at which we process sensory information. The faster the brainwaves, the faster information are processed, the higher the number of captured mental snapshots, and the slower time appears to pass. That is similar to how we capture a fast action scene in slow motion using an iPhone's fast recording speed. One second containing 40 snapshots will 'stretch' and appear four times longer than one second containing 10 snapshots. A faster information processing speed creates the illusion that time is running slowly. In other words, the perceived speed of time is inversely related to the speed at which our brain processes sensory information and how fast it is absorbing reality. In contrast, when our brain's processing speed is slow, less information is recorded from an event and its duration will shrink, as if time flew. It is very important to keep that inverse relationship in mind, as we will use it later to explain many aspects of time perception.

'A faster information processing speed creates the illusion that time is running slowly'

These mental snapshots are the shortest time intervals that our brain can perceive, in contrast to the 'experienced now' moments that we saw in Chapter one and which are the longest time intervals we can perceive as a whole and still call now. Mental snapshots control how we perceive reality, but unlike the 'now' moments, time intervals of this scale are too short to be experienced or too brief to yield any perception of time flow. This is because our brains do not perceive individual snapshots of the world in isolation but, rather, integrate successive mental snapshots into experienced 'now' moments. These experienced 'now(s)' are embedded in an ongoing stream of consciousness which contribute to our feeling of time continuity. Thus, the experience of the flow of time and the illusion of smooth continuous motion is only an approximation. An 'experienced now' moment actually consists of a rapid flow of successive mental snapshots and integrated time durations that varies between 2 to 5 seconds, but are on average 3 seconds long, as we saw previously. The duration of each 'now' moment that we experience is therefore dependent on the duration of all the mental snapshots that constitute it.

Time is nothing but the speed at which we capture and process sensory information from the ever-changing world around us. The perceived speed of time is so much dependent on the speed at which our brain updates the content of our consciousness, i.e. the speed at which we experience the world. Now, let us look at how brain scientists use that knowledge to explain the various time distortions we encounter daily.

CHAPTER 4

TIME DISTORTIONS

THE FALLIBILITY OF OUR INTERNAL CLOCK

'The Moving Finger writes; and, having writ,
Moves on: nor all thy Piety nor Wit
Shall lure it back to cancel half a Line,
Nor all thy Tears wash out a Word of it'
— Omar Al-Khayyam

An Accidental Discovery

In the winter of 1930, the wife of American physiologist, Hudson Hoagland, became sick with a severe flu and high fever. Dr. Hoagland was curious enough to notice that whenever he left his wife's room for a short while, she complained that he had been gone for a long time. In the interest of scientific investigation, and briefly putting aside his nursing duties, he asked his wife to count to 60, with each count corresponding to what she felt was one second, while he kept a record of her temperature. It is not hard to imagine the irritated look on her face at this suggestion, but his wife accepted and he quickly noticed that the hotter she was, the faster she counted. When her temperature was 38 degrees Celsius, for instance, she counted to 60 in 45 seconds. He repeated the experiment a few more times, presumably in total disregard to his wife's feverish objections, so when her temperature reached 39.5 degrees Celsius, she counted one minute in just 37 seconds. The doctor thought that his wife must have some kind of 'internal clock' inside her brain that ran faster as the fever went up. This, in turn, would have made it seem as though he had been out of the room for a long time because her faster internal clock would have made her feel that more time had elapsed than actually had. To confirm his findings, Dr. Hoagland later went back to the University of Massachusetts where he resided, and subjected his students to high temperatures of up to 65 degrees Celsius, by making them wear heated helmets on their heads, while asking them to guess certain time durations. The results, which were later reproduced in countless other studies, confirmed that raising the brain's temperature can increase the brain's 'internal clock' speed by as much as 20 per cent, causing time durations to stretch subjectively by the same proportion [34].

The Brain's Ticking Clock

Psychologists spent the next few decades trying to understand what made the brain's clock tick. They carried out experiments on mice, pigeons, turtles, cats, monkeys, children, and adults, shocking them with electricity, irritating them with unrelenting sound clicks, and strapping them to heated chairs, all in the hope this would slow down or speed up their internal clocks. It was thought that the brain's internal clock counted time in the range of milliseconds, seconds, and minutes and was at the basis of all skills requiring a sense of timing. Several areas in the brain have, over the years, been suggested as a possible location for that internal clock, and with good arguments for each. However, doctors who performed brain CT scans and surgical dissections were unable to detect a single specific structure for it. There was considerable uncertainty about where in the brain time is processed and it took a huge amount of research for brain scientists to finally begin to understand.

We now know that the brain's internal clock is not based on just one specific area in the brain but on a combination of several interconnected brain regions. These regions are linked by an intricate network of neurons that communicate by firing neurotransmitters between each other. As we saw in the previous chapter, this complex neuron network produces synchronized electrical activity, or brainwaves, that fluctuate in cyclic phases and define how fast the brain processes sensory information i.e. how fast it absorbs the world around us. It is this information processing speed that defines how fast we experience the 'flow' of time. The brain's internal clock is merely an oversimplified metaphor for how fast our brains 'record' the world around us.

With this in mind, the relationship that Dr. Hoagland discovered between brain temperature and the subjective speed of time can be explained. We know that chemical reactions occur more rapidly when heated and the speed of biological processes doubles when the temperature increases by 10 degrees Celsius. Therefore, raising the brain's temperature produces changes in the brain's chemical processes that boost the brain's electrical activity resulting in faster brainwaves and faster processing of reality. This, in turn, causes time intervals to expand and the flow of time to slow down, which explains why Hoagland's wife felt he was gone for too long when her fever was up. This is probably why animals in hibernation can get over that period fairly quickly, as time subjectively runs fast in their brain, as body temperatures and metabolic rates decline, though as you might imagine, this is difficult to verify with a squirrel and practically impossible with a hibernating bear!

It is helpful to think of the brain's information processing speed as forming the basis of an 'internal clock' that ticks faster as the speed of processing sensory information increases, and slower as the processing speed decreases. Our brainwaves define the duration of our mental snapshots and information processing speed, which in turn affects how fast or how slow our internal clock is ticking. The brain's internal clock is similar to the 'clock speed' on a computer microchip processor that determines how many calculations a computer can perform per second (GHz). In theory, the higher the processor's 'clock speed', the faster the computer is at processing information. However, this computer vs. brain comparison is not entirely accurate as there are major differences between the types of information processing that go on inside a human brain, and the computations typically performed by a computer. A calculator, for instance, can perform mathematical calculations much faster than a human brain because our brains are not optimized for calculating square roots, division, or compounded interest calculations. Our brains evolved to track motion and can record a stream of images, figure out that they belong to a ball moving in the air, predict its trajectory, and catch it while simultaneously processing other visual signals needed to avoid obstacles on the way. Brains perform well in areas in which computers perform poorly. To give you an idea of the number of computations that happen in the brain when performing a simple act, such as catching a ball, researchers attempted to simulate similar brain calculations using the K-Supercomputer in Japan, currently the fourth most powerful in the world. It took 40 minutes for the supercomputer to calculate the same brain activity generated by one per cent of the brain working for just one second! Just so you know, the K-supercomputer contains 705,024 processor cores and 1.4 million GB of RAM, yet it still needed 40 minutes to crunch all the data generated by just one second of brain activity. Incidentally, the K-Supercomputer is about the size of a basketball court and consumes as much electricity as a small town of 10,000 suburban homes. In contrast, a human brain's processing power is confined to a skull that is smaller than a basketball, and has a power consumption of about 30 watts that can barely power a small light bulb!

The Internal Clock Model

The most popular model for the brain's internal clock was developed by psychologist Michel Treisman in 1963 and is composed of two facets: a clock and a counter. In the clock facet, a hypothetical clock is ticking at a certain speed that we now know corresponds to the brain's speed of processing sensory information. As the internal clock ticks, a counter counts these ticks and keeps a record in memory of how much time has elapsed. The speed of the hypothetical internal clock is influenced by several factors such as the level of alertness, emotions, personality traits, and age, among others. We will cover each of these factors in more detail in subsequent chapters. For now, it is sufficient to keep in mind that a fast processing of reality is like a fast ticking internal clock.

To illustrate that, imagine that your brain's electrical activity is running at a level that allows sensory information to be processed 50% faster than usual. Let us imagine that you just finished reading a long article in the newspaper that took 10 minutes to read but, not having a watch in your hand, you are not really sure how long you have been reading. When 10 minutes of 'real' time have elapsed, your fast running internal clock would have ticked 50% more time and would have covered 15 minutes of experienced duration. This means that from your point of view, those 10 real minutes would appear to contain five more minutes and would seem longer than usual, so the time spent reading that article appears to have dragged. On the other hand, if your brain's processing speed and internal clock were running 50% slower than usual, it would subjectively tick less time and count only 5 minutes when 10 minutes of real time have actually elapsed. Therefore, from your perspective, those 10 real minutes would appear to be 5 minutes shorter than usual. Reading that article during those 10 minutes will be over sooner than you expect and you will wonder how time flew. This inverse relationship might sound counter-intuitive and confusing, but it is easy to remember. A fast ticking internal clock creates the illusion that time is running slow while a slower one will produce the feeling that time is flying.

In the counter facet of the internal clock model, on the other hand, you can imagine a hypothetical counter that counts the emitted ticks from the internal clock and compares them to the real objective duration or to some previously reinforced duration stored in memory. The internal clock's counter represents the level of attention we deliberately devote to track the passage of time and acts like a gate that opens wider or narrower depending on that level of attention. Consider the case of waiting 30 minutes for an important meeting, for instance. Attention to time is high and the attention gate is wide open allowing more ticks to be counted compared to a case where attention to time is not important, such as reading a book. While reading, attention is distracted from tracking time, the counter gate is therefore narrower and starts missing some of the emitted clock ticks, so the reading time will seem short. Since our experience of an interval's duration depends on the number of ticks counted by our internal clock's counter, it follows then that the same time interval of 30 minutes will feel longer when in a waiting situation and shorter while reading.

The attention counter is crucial when the time aspect is highly relevant, such as when you are facing a deadline, waiting for a specific event to occur, eager for an event to continue or end, or experiencing time stress. When more attention is devoted to track time, the counter gate opens wide allowing more ticks to be counted so the perceived duration seems longer and time appear to be running slow. In contrast, when we are engaged in activities that distract us from tracking time, such as when absorbed in a good book or movie, the attention to time is low and the counter gate is narrow, counting less ticks. Therefore, the experienced duration is shorter than actual duration and time seems to fly. We will explore the role of attention on time perception in more detail in the next chapter and understand why sayings like 'a watched pot never boils' and 'time flies when you are having fun' are very true.

"When the brain's internal clock speeds up, time seems to drag. When it slows down, time flies"

Time Mismatches

Time is a reflection of how fast we process sensory information and capture mental snapshots from reality. The internal clock model is a useful tool that helps us picture how time subjectively speeds up or slows down. In the internal clock model, the clock's ticking speed is a metaphor of our brain's processing speed and duration of our mental snapshots. When the mental snapshots are short, the internal clock would tick faster. The speed at which the brain processes mental snapshots and the speed of the internal clock are two ways of looking at the same thing and will be used interchangeably in this book. In the internal clock model, the counter gate represents the level of attention we devote to track the passage of time and keeps a record of the number of ticks emitted by the hypothetical internal clock (or amount of information processed by the brain). The 'experienced duration' is made up of successive experienced 'now' moments, and each one of those are in turn made up of a series of mental snapshots. When we stop at the end of an activity and wonder how long it has been going on, we often find that the experienced duration does not match the real duration. As a result, we experience a psychological time mismatch. As an example, it is late in the evening and you have just finished watching the latest blockbuster movie at the cinema that runs for one hour. You were so absorbed with the movie that, when you check your watch, you are pleasantly surprised to find that it is earlier than you had thought as it felt like time had flown by. Imagine you had, instead, been attending a boring corporate dinner event. You know what that feels like: checking your watch to discover that only one hour has passed when it felt like you arrived ages ago. In both cases, the same one-hour time interval you subjectively estimated in your mind was the 'experienced duration' of the activity you were engaged in and, depending on the situation, it felt shorter or longer than the real one-hour duration. This divergence from the real objective duration creates a psychological mismatch and a feeling that the flow of time has been somehow distorted. It is as if our internal clock was ticking faster or slower than real clocks causing time to fly or drag. It is similar to the experience of flying in a plane where you only feel the motion of the plane during take-off or landing. That is because the plane is accelerating or decelerating relative to the ground. However, it is not easy to detect motion when the plane is already up and flying at a constant speed. When the plane reaches its altitude and its speed is constant, you look out from your window and feel as if the plane is not moving at all. In the same way, you realize that the flow of time has been somehow distorted when the perceived speed of time runs faster or slower than the objective external time as measured by a good external clock. It is this kind of time distortion that we would want to control so as to speed up or slow down the perceived passage of time to our needs.

Harnessing the Power of our Internal Clock

So it is clear that we do not perceive time the same way wall clocks depict time. Subjective time does not flow at a steady rate. Not all hours are equal. Perceived time intervals are elastic in nature, stretching and shrinking in our mind. Most of the time, our internal clock is ticking either more slowly or more quickly, depending on how fast we are processing sensory information, i.e. how fast we are recording mental snapshots in our mind. Sometimes entire moments are missed, as if they were never part of our life. Whenever our subjective experience of time is different from the objective passing of time, a psychological time distortion occurs. Such time mismatches can be quite useful if we can control and induce them at will. If you are, for instance, going on a long trip and have nothing to do, you would want to kill time so that the trip passes swiftly. If you were going through a period of pain, it would help to perceive that painful period as being as short as possible. In both cases you want to record as few mental snapshots as possible. In contrast, if you are really enjoying a nice dinner with your date or having a good time with some friends, you might want to slow down time so that the experience lasts longer. You can make every second count by capturing the largest number of snapshots possible. Wouldn't it be nice if we could voluntarily extend a moment of bliss or shorten a moment of pain according to our needs? Wouldn't it be great if we could slow down time so that we subjectively live longer?

The Roman philosopher Seneca wrote 2,000 year ago, 'You must match time's swiftness with your speed in using it, and you must drink quickly as though from a rapid stream that will not always flow'. This is probably the wisest advice of all time. The sentiment expressed in those words embodies the view that time runs so fast that you need to prepare your mind and be constantly alert to tap into its swift flow, control its speed, and make best use of that scarce resource. There is obviously nothing we can do to change the real speed of time or the actual time it takes for something to occur, but we can control our experience of the time it takes and this is what really matters. This can only be done by manipulating the speed of our brain's internal clock and our attention counter, i.e. the speed at which we record mental snapshots and how many of those are retained in our memory. The question is then, if the subjective speed of time is inversely related to the brain's information processing speed and level of electrical activity, how can that be increased or decreased? How can we boost the speed at which our brain records the world so as to slow down time? Is there anything we can do to boost our brain's electrical activity and speed of our brainwaves? Are there any special situations that cause the brain's processing speed, and hence the speed of the internal clock, to dramatically change? Do we all experience the same subjective speed of time or does time run faster for some and slower for others? If the answer to the latter is yes, what individual differences are involved in our time perception? Essentially, how can we slow down or speed up our experience of time?

We saw that fever can speed up the internal clock and slow down time. To achieve a similar effect without actually getting sick, we will need to understand what other factors affect the speed at which we perceive reality. In the second part of this book and over the next 5 chapters, we will explore some of these factors starting with:

1. Living in the Moment: How Does Attention Affect our Perception of Time?

2. Time in Slow Motion: The Effect of Alertness

3. Taking Control: The Effect of Emotions

4. What Kind of Person are you? The Effect of Personality Traits

5. Messing with Time: The Effect of Drugs and Mental Disorders

Each of these factors, affect the brain's processing speed in a special way and influence our subjective speed of time differently. We will discuss and derive practical applications from that knowledge that will help us control the speed of time. We will then look at how our brains perceive the past and future, and from that will be able to explore the most important factor, which is the effect of age on the speed of time. Let us now press on with the role of attention.

PART TWO

WHAT FACTORS INFLUENCE OUR TIME EXPERIENCE?

CHAPTER 5

LIVING IN THE MOMENT

HOW DOES ATTENTION AFFECT OUR TIME EXPERIENCE?

'A Watched Pot Never Boil'
— Popular Idiom

Attention to Time

In the fall of 1980, at the Augusta College in Georgia, a group of students wait in a room to start an experiment. One by one, the students are taken individually into another room that has a coffee pot filled with water on a stove. The scientist conducting the experiment tells some students, 'There will be a delay in starting the experiment. I will return for you when we are ready. Would you mind calling me in the other room when the water starts boiling? Thanks.' Other students are told the same thing, but without any reference to the boiling water. After 4 minutes, the experimenter returns and asks the participants to guess how much time has elapsed. He notes that those who watched the water pot felt that they waited longer compared to those who did not. The fact that they were anticipating the water to boil caused time to pass slowly! As we saw earlier, this is referred to as a *prospective* time experience, because the participants were fully aware of the passing time. As it turns out, the popular saying 'a watched pot never boils' has a lot of truth in it [35].

This chapter is about the attention we devote to the passage of time and how that slows it down. It is also about how any form of distraction from the passage of time can speed it up. Time is information and, like any type of information, requires mental focus and attention to process it. One aspect of being attentive is the ability to focus on a specific object and tune out any surrounding distractions. We have all, for instance, experienced how things taste better when we close our eyes. Focusing on the taste of a great ice-cream melting in your mouth, while your eyes are closed, creates a more intense tasting experience because, when the sense of vision is shut down, the brain can dedicate more processing power to the sense of taste. Forced attention always brings more intensity to whatever we are attending to. This is why a heightened sense of attention to the present moment will make it seem longer and more intense. In the hypothetical internal clock model, we can think of it as a wide open counter that is counting more time than usual. Let us look at a few typical examples.

When you are sitting in a waiting room or standing in a long queue waiting for your turn to arrive, your attention to the passage of time will make 10 minutes seem like an hour. When you are bored, you are constantly looking at your watch and time seems to pass by excruciatingly slowly. On the other hand, if you are totally absorbed in a certain activity that you really enjoy, like reading a fascinating book, more attention is devoted to that activity and less attention is directed to the passage of time, and it feels like time flew. Consider, for instance, how time seems to drag when a receptionist puts you on hold over the phone. As you wait on the line, you become sharply aware of time-related signals or cues. You may engage in some kind of timekeeping strategy such as tapping with your feet, drumming your fingers on the table, or silently counting the seconds. You could be pacing the floor, back and forth, performing a series of repetitive movements, or simply staring at the moving hands of a clock. Whatever you do, this attentiveness to time dramatically alters your experience of time, causing it to drag.

We experience a similar time-expanding effect in activities where time is highly relevant. If you are attending a very important event that starts at a specific time, and you do not want to be late, time will be highly relevant on the way there and, as your awareness of the passing time will be high, the trip will feel longer. On the way back, although it is the same distance, you will feel the trip to be quicker, since time is no longer relevant [36]. Studies conducted on people who experience earthquakes show that people often report the duration of earthquakes to be in the range of minutes when the actual duration is normally in the range of 30 to 40 seconds. The passage of time during an earthquake is highly relevant since it is a major threat and the person experiencing it wants it to end. Their focus on the question 'when it will be over?' forces a heightened attention to time, which causes them to perceive the duration as longer than it actually is. Fear also causes them to be more alert, which as we shall see in a later chapter, also causes the time interval to subjectively expand.

Another example is how time drags when waiting on a red traffic signal to turn green. Some cities in Europe have countdown timers installed on red lights to indicate the remaining time before turning green. Such counters enhance the drivers' awareness of time and make their waiting seem even longer. In addition to red signal countdown timers, countdowns are popular on green signals in a few Chinese cities. They are used to indicate how much time a driver has before it turns red. The idea is that this would help drivers decide whether to slow down and stop, or speed up and cross the intersection. However, these countdown timers tend to increase the drivers' awareness of time, causing them to over-estimate the time they have left before red appears. This has actually led to an increase in red light violations on intersections with these timers! For this reason, traffic authorities in most U.S cities prohibit the use of timers for car traffic, and only pedestrian timers are used.

Whether you are waiting for a friend to join you, for a traffic light to turn green, or a call center to respond, time awareness is high when you are in anticipation of something happening. As a result, durations appear to stretch, and the flow of time seems to run slowly.

Distraction from Time

At the beginning of the 20th century, when lifts were first introduced in high-rise buildings, many people complained that they were too slow. Rather than redesign the lift motors, engineers came up with a quick clever fix. They started installing mirrors in the lift cabins to give people something to look at while they waited. The same lift journeys now felt shorter since people could check on their appearance instead of staring at their watch!

In contrast to how time drags when we devote attention to it, time flies when attention is distracted away from it. When we are having a good time with our friends, watching an enjoyable movie, or absorbed in a good book, we lose track of time and that activity is over in a blink. If you are going through a hectic day where you are constantly running from one thing to another, oblivious to the passage of time, that day will be over before you know it. Contrast that with a day spent at home with not much to do. That day will crawl along slowly, and seem longer because you can afford to devote some attention to the passage of time and that slows time's apparent speed. Busy time goes by quickly. Empty time goes by slowly.

As we saw in the previous chapter, one way to explain how this happens is to use the internal clock model and imagine that our attention acts as a counter that counts the number of ticks emitted by our brain's internal clock. When you devote more attention to the passage of time, the attention counter gate is wide open and, as a result, none of the ticks emitted by your brain's internal clock are missed, so that more time is counted and the duration of that activity will seem long, so time appears to drag. On the other hand, when your attention is distracted from time keeping, the attention counter gate becomes narrow and starts missing some of the ticks emitted by your internal clock. The result is that less time is counted and the duration of that activity will seem shorter, so time flies.

Another way to illustrate that is to imagine a bank that has two security cameras monitoring its entrance. Both cameras capture the scene of a man walking down the street for a period of 10 seconds and at a speed of 20 snapshots or frames per second (fps). As a result, both cameras record a film of 200 snapshots of the man. Now let us assume that the second camera is not just filming the walking man, but has to divert some of its attention to capture another event inside the bank, simultaneously. The second camera takes one snapshot of the walking man, followed by one snapshot of the bank event, then one snapshot of the walking man, and so on. Later on, the second camera film is taken to the cutting room to create the scene of the walking man. When the images of the walking man are cut and combined together, that scene will contain only 100 snapshots spread over 10 seconds that looks as if it was recorded at the speed of 10 snapshots per second (10 fps). When the scenes from each film are compared, you will conclude that the flow of time is faster in the second film, as if the man was walking in fast forward mode. That is because the images in the first film are replayed at the normal speed of 20 fps in which they were recorded, while the images in the second film show a larger change between each other due to the missing snapshots. In the same manner, when we have to divide our attention so that we are paying less attention to the passing time, our brain's internal clock misses some of the ticks and the time intervals seem shorter as if time was running fast.

To recap, when you are aware of the passing time, your brain counts more time, and durations expand in your mind as if time slowed down. On the other hand, if you are engaged in a complex task that requires your full attention, your brain cannot afford to pay any attention to time, less time is counted and durations shrink in your mind as if time flew. So how can we use this knowledge to slow down or speed up the subjective flow of time?

'Busy time goes fast. Empty time goes slow'

Slowing Down Time with Mindfulness

Slowing down time can be done using the technique of 'mindfulness', which is the practice of cultivating a focused awareness on the present moment. Mindfulness is used for treating mental health issues but can be quite useful when you are having a good time and want it to last longer. Mindfulness is defined as having moment-to-moment awareness of what is happening around you, essentially 'living in the moment'. It is commonly achieved through meditation, although people can be mindful in almost any situation. Buddhist monks who practice mindfulness meditation often report a slowing down of time. By closing their eyes and focusing on the present moment, they ignore the outside world and experience expanding time durations. People who practice mindfulness focus their attention internally, such as on one's breathing or heartbeat, or externally on an object, while being fully aware of the present moment. This shift of focus on the 'here and now' boosts attention levels so that time durations are stretched and time runs slowly [37, 38].

Evidence for this time-slowing effect comes from people who report an enhanced appreciation of music after performing mindfulness meditation. In a 2011 study at Duke University Center for Mindfulness Research, researchers had one group of students listen to a 10-minute excerpt from Puccini's opera *La Boheme,* after practicing 15 minutes of mindfulness meditation. Another group listened to the same musical piece but without prior meditation. The results of the study showed that students who meditated before listening had a more satisfying and engaging musical experience compared to students who did not meditate first [39]. These results are to be expected since mindfulness enhances attention and focuses the mind on the present moment, so that time slows down and every musical note becomes more intense. The outcome is an effortless oneness with the music, a sense of being 'in the zone' with the music. We will also later see how music is more enjoyable when under the influence of drugs (e.g. weed), for the same reason that these stimulants slow down time. However, you do not have to go to such extremes to heighten your musical appreciation. Simply being mindful can produce the same effect.

You can, therefore, make a pleasant activity seem longer by intentionally being mindful of every passing moment and every fleeting detail. Such attention to time will cause that activity to slow down and its duration to stretch. Similar time-controlling tips will be combined into the last chapter, which will be focused on crafting the longest year of your life.

'Living in the moment slows down time'

Speeding up Time: The Power of Distraction

In contrast, if you want to speed up time you should try to shift your focus away from the passage of time. This is a strategy that all shopping malls, amusement parks, and call centers deliberately use to make people feel they have not spent as long engaging in that particular activity as they actually have. The reason for this is that if people feel they have been waiting or shopping for a long time, they might leave and not buy anything. In such venues, durations are shortened by diverting attention away from time into other interesting or attractive distractions. For example, call centers play background music and amusement park operators install TV screens or have clowns walk around the queue lines. This cleverly diverts attention from time and makes the wait seem shorter. In situations where routines cannot be abandoned, companies and schools have considered eliminating unnecessary wall clocks or reminders of time as an effective means of reducing time awareness and promoting intrinsic motivation. Therefore, in situations where you want time to run fast, you should distract yourself from time. But do not abandon your wristwatch already as you might start missing your appointments. Rather, focus on the task in hand, regardless of how boring it is, so that your attention is diverted from the passage of time and it will be over in a blink.

"Time flies when you are having fun." This saying is so entrenched in our mind that the converse is also true: 'you are having fun when time flies'. When you feel that time has passed unexpectedly quickly, you will most likely judge an activity as more entertaining. People assume that if time flew, then the experience must have been fun. Conversely, when people feel that time is dragging, they evaluate the experience as unpleasant. If you were chatting with a friend for 5 minutes and were later told that the conversation had lasted 15 minutes, you would be surprised at how time had flown, and would feel that the conversation was enjoyable. If, on the other hand, you were chatting for 15 minutes but were later told that only 5 minutes had passed, you would feel that time had dragged and you would judge the conversation negatively. This effect was confirmed in a study done at the University of St. Thomas in Minneapolis where researchers asked students to do a little task that involved reading a text and underlining all word with double letter combinations, like apple and bottle. The duration of the task was going to be exactly 10 minutes for all students, but that is not what they were told. Half of the students were told they will spend only five minutes, while the other half were told they will be doing the task for 20 minutes. These deceptions created a feeling of surprise later on when the students were told their time was up. Those students who were told they will be doing the task for 5 minutes felt it was taking forever. Meanwhile, the students who though they were working for 20 minutes felt that duration pass in a breeze. They were tricked into thinking it had lasted half as long. The researchers then asked the participants how much they enjoyed this mundane task. Those who felt time fly rated the task much more enjoyable than the participants who felt that time dragged; even though both groups had actually experienced the same boring task for exactly the same 10-minutes time duration!

The researchers also made the students listen to the irritating noise of a dot-matrix printer while observing a timer counting the elapsed time on a computer screen. Behind the scenes, the researchers manipulated the speed of time by either accelerating or decelerating the timer by 20 per cent to give the illusion that time was either flying or dragging. The results were consistent: students who were under the illusion that time flew evaluated the noise as less irritating than those students who were under the illusion that time dragged, even though both groups endured the annoying noise for the same duration [40]. The study showed just how important the subjective speed of time is to our evaluation of how much we enjoy life. Whenever we are surprised by the way time flew, we tend to fall back on that old cliché and assume that the reason for this time distortion was that we must have been having fun. This brings us to the important mental state of consciousness called 'flow' where time really flies.

Experiencing 'Flow': A State of Consciousness

Have you ever started reading a book in the morning and, a little while later, noticed it was already getting dark? Or spent half an hour playing a video game which, afterwards, you find actually lasted 3 hours? Have you ever experienced a time in your life when you were so absorbed in what you were doing that the rest of the world seemed to have disappeared? A situation where you were totally focused on an activity, so much so that you were not even aware of yourself; as if time itself ceased to exist and only when you were done did you realize how much time had actually passed? If you answered yes, then you have experienced a state of consciousness that psychologists call 'flow'.

Flow is the exact opposite of boredom. It is a special mental state that was first studied in detail by world-famous psychologist Mihály Csíkszentmihályi when he became fascinated by artists, especially painters, who seemed so immersed in what they were doing that their sense of time was twisted. The best illustration comes from Csíkszentmihályi himself (you can give up trying to pronounce his name). Imagine you are skiing down a challenging slope and fully focused on every move you make. The trees, the curves, and the freezing air in your face. Your attention is so focused as not to allow any distractions. The run is flawless and you do not want it to end. It may have taken 15 minutes in real time, but felt like it was over in a blink. Such experience happen all the time in sports such as soccer, tennis, dancing, running, or while being absorbed in hobbies such as painting, drawing, writing, or playing chess. Experiences of full immersion can also occur in the workplace or during an interesting social interaction, such as talking with a close friend. We become completely absorbed in what we are doing, with a feeling of energized focus, motivation, and intrinsic satisfaction.

Actions performed during a flow experience are effortless and stand out as exceptional moments in life. You feel that things are exactly as you want them to be and cannot be any better. The experience in such moments is so intense when compared to the unexciting backdrop of daily routine. You lose awareness of yourself and become one with whatever you are doing. A piano player merges with the instrument and becomes the music he is playing. A painter is absorbed by his painting and is transported to a different realm of consciousness. People describe such experiences with expressions like 'in the groove' or 'getting lost in the book' so that we 'forget ourselves'. Athletes use the term 'being in the zone', artists describe 'aesthetic ruptures', or a 'heightened state of consciousness', and religious mystics refer to it as a state of 'ecstasy'.

Many famous artists and sports figures are known to perform only when in a state of flow or when 'in the zone'. Historical sources suggest that Michelangelo may have painted the ceiling of the Vatican's Sistine Chapel while in such a mental state. Some say he painted for days at a time and was so absorbed by his work that he lost track of time. He did not even eat or sleep until he passed out. He would then wake up re-energized and start to paint again in a state of complete absorption. Likewise, the great Formula 1 champion, Ayrton Senna, was also known to experience flow during races. In an excerpt from an interview that he gave during the qualification rounds for the 1988 Monaco Grand Prix, he describes his flow experience: "I was already on pole and I just kept going. Suddenly I was nearly two seconds faster than anybody else, including my team mate with the same car. And suddenly I realized that I was no longer driving the car consciously. I was driving it by a kind of instinct, only I was in a different dimension. It was like I was in a tunnel" [41]. But what is it about flow experiences that makes time run so much faster?

The common element in all flow experiences is the focused attention and total absorption in an activity, which diverts attention from the passing time, causing it to pass swiftly. The amount of information that can be processed by our brains within a certain time interval is limited by the level of electrical activity and brain processing speed. We are therefore constantly making a tradeoff between what we are paying attention to out of the huge variety of possibilities. While in a state of flow, the focus is so intense that discomforts are not felt and negative thoughts do not enter the mind. The brain is too busy focusing on that activity to keep track of those other things. Nearly all of our brain's available processing power is devoted to one activity and very little is available to time keeping. As a result, the attention counter gate of our internal clock gets narrow and starts missing the ticks emitted. This causes activity durations to seem shorter and thus time runs faster.

'The common element in all 'flow' experiences is the total absorption, which diverts attention from the passing time causing it to pass swiftly'

At the University of York, a study was undertaken in 2013 with students playing Tetris. This is a computer maze game in which the degree of immersion was manipulated by adding or omitting the music soundtrack from the game. The students were then asked to estimate how long they played for. They found that students who had the music on felt that they played for less time than those who played without the music [42]. Music made playing more immersive requiring more attention to the game, so the players paid less attention to time and felt a shorter duration of play. Video games challenge players' skills and grab their attention. The complexity of play, the need for quick thinking and fast reaction, coordinating motor skills, all require high levels of concentration so less attention is available to track time. Once players are engrossed in the game, they also go through a highly rewarding and entertaining experience that increases motivation which then pulls them into playing more in a positive feedback loop. Those feedback loops repeat several times during each session, reducing time awareness and leading to the feeling that time flew.

Encouraging 'Flow': Motivation, Goals, and Challenges

An equally significant aspect of flow-inducing activities is the required level of motivation, since this affects the amount of fun generated. Fun comes in two types. There is low-motivation passive fun such as relaxing on a beach, enjoying the tranquil serenity of a natural scene, and media consumption like watching a movie or TV. And there is high-motivation active fun that involves elements of desire and excitement that motivate us to act, such as adventure activities, hobbies, social interactions, and sports. Researchers find that time flies much more quickly when fun is of the second type, i.e. highly motivated and goal-oriented fun. They also agree that greater satisfaction is produced in high-motivation activities that involve a challenge to achieve a certain goal and a reward for that accomplishment.

To investigate this, researchers came up with an interesting experiment to understand how the two aspects of fun affect our time experience. At the University of Alabama, psychology students were shown pleasant images that were either low on motivation (like flowers) or high on motivation (like desirable desserts) and had to determine which images were displayed for the longest time. As expected, students felt that the flower images were displayed for a longer duration than the enticing dessert images [43]. What was even more interesting was that the duration of desirable cake images was perceived to be shorter in direct relation to the amount of time it had been since the students last ate. Students who were hungry had high motivation for food, and so they judged the dessert images as passing more quickly compared to students who had eaten recently. The greater the desire and motivation, the faster time passed. This confirms that time flies when we are engaged in activities that involve active high-motivation happiness. Just being content or satisfied does not speed up time as much, but being excited and actively pursuing the things you desire does.

Activities involving high-motivation challenge and rewards occur when people are doing their favorite hobbies like gardening, bowling, painting, playing chess, or cooking a good meal. However, very rarely do people report flow in passive leisure activities, such as relaxing or watching television. In fact, television distracts the brain without creating the kind of challenge that can lead to flow. According to scientists, due to the low-motivation, you would have to watch TV for 15,000 hours to generate 30 minutes of brain activity! Whereas reading for 10 minutes is much more mentally engaging because it fires up the imagination and stimulates the kind of brain activity that promotes flow. So how do we enter the state of flow and speed up time?

People tend to experience flow when facing a set of clear goals with specific rules. Examples of this might be tennis, chess, or poker, because these games have set objectives and rules with intrinsic rewards that put players in a self-contained world. The same happens when someone is playing a musical instrument, performing a religious ritual, or climbing a mountain. To enter flow, you have to set a goal that you want to achieve. Once the goal and challenges are clearly defined, you should work on possessing the skills that perfectly match those challenges. The optimal goal is the one that balances your skills against the challenge and keeps you fully engaged. Let us say that you have always wanted to play the guitar. An early beginner course will be boring if you already know how to play. When the challenge is low, you will be bored, the outcome is relaxed, and time will drag. If you have had a few beginners' lessons, this course would be easy. You might not be bored but you would not be stimulated or experience flow. As a complete novice, you would be stretched but would also feel motivated and satisfied. Being constantly stretched is where you want to be. It is what keeps you in a state of flow and speeds up time. The crucial factors in 'flow' are total absorption, full engagement of skills, focused attention on achieving the goal, and intrinsic motivation for the reward. With this in mind, almost any activity, no matter how dull it is, can produce flow. Let us now look at the time spent at work, for instance, and how to induce the kind of flow that makes it time worth spending.

Creating a Sense of 'Flow' at Work and Leisure

Most people have times in their lives when they see work as something dull, stressful, and meaningless. If we had the chance, most of us would prefer to work less. Nevertheless, time spent at work does not have to be that way. In fact, research shows that people find more 'flow' on the job than in free time. This is to be expected, since work usually has clear objectives and rules of performance that are lacking in free time. It also has reward in the form of bonuses and satisfaction in the form of achievements.

If you are not happy with the time you spend at work, you need to find ways to create a state of flow in what you do. This involves paying close attention to every detail of your job and asking yourself how it can be done in a faster and more efficient way. You could be a receptionist, a doctor, an accountant, or a construction engineer. Regardless, you need to convert a dull routine job into a meaningful one that fulfills your need for novelty and personal accomplishment. You have to set clear goals and challenges that match your skills. If the challenge is too easy for your skills, you will not find any satisfaction in accomplishing it. If the challenge is too hard, you will have to either learn new skills, get help, or else risk being stressed. Viewing your work as a goal by itself will allow you to enjoy life while being responsible to others in society. Buddhist writings advise us to "act always as if the future of the universe depended on what you did, while laughing at yourself for thinking that whatever you do makes any difference." With this in mind, work can be both serious and playful, making it possible to be both responsibly engaged and carefree at the same time. And what about free time? After a long hard week at work, you finally get to the weekend; how can you find a state of flow in that?

When spending time at home with your family or alone, there is no clear goal or purpose. No skills are involved in enjoying free time, which is why most people find it hard to find flow when they have nothing specific that engages their attention. Free time is sometimes harder to enjoy than work! From an evolutionary perspective, we inherited a nervous system from our ancestors that has evolved to expect dangers, obstacles, and challenges and is not used to prolonged periods of free time. Having leisure time in abundance does not automatically mean endless fun. Perfect examples are some multi-millionaires who do not have to work and have all the free time in the world. Yet, when that time is devoid of goals and challenges, it becomes meaningless, often leading to depression and addictions. Therefore, to enhance our quality of life, we need to learn how to use our free time in achieving goals that contribute to our life satisfaction and doing the things we enjoy.

As we saw, leisure time can be active (high-motivation), like playing sports, doing exercise, creating art, making music, engaging in conversation, or it can be passive (low-motivation), like media consumption, watching TV and movies, listening to music, or lying on the beach. We saw in Chapter 1 how spending our free time on certain activities can be considered a waste if it does not add much to life fulfillment. This is not to say that spending time on passive leisure is a poor use of time. Of course, peaceful relaxation can be exceedingly rewarding, but being immersed in a challenge is more likely to make us happy and will be perceived as time that is well spent. Flow-inducing activities also create richer memories or 'memory markers' when compared to passive fun activities. You might enjoy watching TV for a couple of hours, but a few days later, when you try to recall that time, there may be no trace of it in your memory. Whereas, a couple of hours spent on a hiking trip could produce many more memories that will last for years in your mind. In a later chapter, we shall explore in more detail how creating memory markers is critical to the way we perceive our time in the past and essential to our overall life satisfaction. They enrich our past causing it to appear longer than it really is. In contrast, passive fun does not create enough memory anchors so that it appears shorter than it really is retrospectively.

A recent study by Csíkszentmihályi and his team found that American teenagers experience a mental state of flow only 13 percent of the time when watching TV, but 34 percent of the time when doing their favorite hobbies and 44 percent of the time when they are involved in sports or games [44]. As expected active leisure has a higher potential to produce states of flow than passive leisure. But what is strange is that those same teenagers prefer to spend more of their free time staring at a screen of some kind than doing sports or performing their hobbies! The same results apply to adults. Why is that? Why do we spend more of our free time doing something that has little chance of making us feel good?

The answer is that an activity that produces a state of flow normally requires an initial investment of attention and dedication before it begins to be entertaining. If you play the piano, for instance, you will recall that before you actually started enjoying this flow-inducing activity, you had to endure at least an hour of tedious practice every day. If you are a good tennis player that often gets into the 'zone' while playing, you would remember the long hours you had to spend practicing to reach the level you are at. It takes some effort to become a musician, poet, explorer, inventor, scientist, or artist that can spend time in a state of flow. So if you lack the dedication and discipline to surmount the initial hurdle, you will likely settle for something that, like watching TV, is less entertaining but more accessible. However remember that every second you spend honing a flow-inducing skill goes a long way into making your free time less boring and more enjoyable. The initial effort might seem too much but it is well worth it. Csíkszentmihályi, author of the book *Flow*, puts it well when he says: 'The best moments in our lives are not the passive, receptive, relaxing times. The best moments usually occur when our minds are stretched to their limits in a voluntary effort to accomplish something difficult and worthwhile'. It is the full immersion in flow experiences, rather than passive happiness, which makes for excellence in life.

Recap

Let us sum up what we have covered so far. Time slows down or speeds up in direct proportion to the degree of attention and mental focus we devote to its passing. When we are aware of the passing time, the 'experienced duration' expands and time slows down, as is evident from activities that involve an element of anticipation or a heightened awareness of time. When our attention is distracted from tracking time, the experienced duration shrinks and time flies. Due to our limited span of attention, the more difficult or complex the thing you are doing, the more distracted we will be from tracking time and the faster time goes by.

To slow down time, be mindful and focus on the present moment. To speed up boring situations, avoid time cues or anything that makes you aware of the passing of time. Focus instead on the activity in hand and it will pass more quickly. Living the perfect moment involves a mental state of total absorption, relaxed focus, and gratification. This is referred to as a state of 'flow' and it occurs when we are mindfully immersed in an activity to the extent that we become totally oblivious to the passage of time. It might sound contradictory, but to make the most of your time, lose track of it. This means living in the moment in a state of total engagement, relaxed focus and gratification to the extent that you are not aware of that moment. Activities that produce flow can occur at work, during leisure time, and in almost any situation that involves clear goals, challenges with matching skill level, and immediate reward. Low-motivation passive activities, like watching TV or relaxing on the beach, are necessary sometimes, but do not produce the same satisfaction as high-motivation active and flow-inducing activities.

It is now time to look at another very important factor that affects our time perception, which, when taken to extremes, can almost freeze time altogether!

CHAPTER 6

TIME IN SLOW MOTION

THE EFFECT OF ALERTNESS

'As an object hurtles through space, time is altered relative
to its motion and speed'
— Albert von St. Gallen Heim

The Timing of Amazing Athletes

Few baseball players in the history of the Major League were as skilled at batting as Hall of Famer, Tony Gwynn. During the course of his baseball career, Gwynn would cause nightmares for his pitching opponents, wielding his bat to produce record-breaking statistics. To the audience, a typical ball would be whizzing and curving towards the plate at around 100 mph, faster than the eye can see but, to Gwynn, it seemed like it was in slow motion as he hit it with extreme ease. His intent fixation on the ball, his determined focus tuning out any distractions around him, and his deep concentration, somehow enabled him to perceive the whizzing ball as if time had slowed down. No wonder Gwynn has often been referred to as the greatest hitter since Ted Williams. Other famous athletes and sports stars, such as Tiger woods in golf, Michael Jordan in basketball, and Roger Federer in tennis, often report similar experiences. In these games, talented players seem to experience the ball coming toward them much more slowly than average people do. So what is happening here? What is so different about their brains that allow them to control the speed of time and slow it down to their advantage?

As we have seen in Chapter 3, the perceived speed of time depends on how fast our brain can process sensory information and how fast it 'records' the world around us. That information processing speed relies on the level of brain electrical activity which, in turn, is a reflection of how alert and attentive we are. Psychologists refer to alertness as 'mental arousal' which is a measure of how fast we are able to react to external stimulations. Alertness and attention are very closely related, since the level of alertness determines how much attention we can focus on a task. They both depend on how energized or tired we are and on the level of electrical activity in our brain that is measured as EEG brainwaves.

When brain neurons are excited, they produce a sharp state of alertness and focused attention that can considerably influence our time perception. Higher levels of mental arousal mean that the brain is more sensitive to detecting information, processing, and retrieving it from memory. Processing more information in a shorter period causes time to stretch and can explain why successful sport people, with their higher innate level of alertness and excellent concentration skills, perceive time as running slower than normal. They perform such amazing feats because of their superior focus and faster information processing (faster ticking internal clock) that stretches time intervals. This produces the experience that time must have been running slow.

Sport scientists have discovered that athletes' alpha brainwave frequency tend to be naturally higher than average people, especially before peak performances. Golfers and basketball players experience bursts of alpha brainwaves shortly before their best shots. In one study, researchers measured the brainwaves of karate champions and fencing experts at rest, with their eyes closed, and compared them with ordinary people. The results indicated that the athletes generally emit stronger alpha brainwaves, which implies they can react and process sensory information faster [45]. Their brain engine is essentially running at a higher rpm when idle at rest. The result is a faster internal clock and a sense that time is flowing more slowly. Illegal performance-enhancing drugs and stimulants that are often used in sports produce the same effect on alertness and information processing speeds, causing time to slow down. This will be considered further in Chapter 10.

Scientists also found that professional athletes can detect faster flickering lights compared to an average person. We previously saw how houseflies and birds that detect extremely fast flickering lights experience time in slow motion. Well, famous athletes may not come close to beating a fly's flicker limit, but their eyes possess an enhanced ability to track fast-moving balls during games. This allows them to process the motion of the ball at a higher temporal resolution, and forces their flow of time to expand, allowing them relatively ample time to react. Ted Williams, arguably the greatest baseball hitter of all-time, once said he could see the laces on a baseball flying at 90 mph!

The Alertness Spectrum

Our alertness level is directly related to our brain's electrical activity and EEG brainwaves which, in turn, determine the speed at which we 'record' the world, and define how fast we experience time. Using EEG recordings, researchers in Germany confirmed in 2012 that the apparent speed of time varies depending on where we are on the spectrum of conscious experience [46]. The more alert we are, the slower time seems to run and vice versa. In one study, participants were requested to estimate time intervals while connected to EEG scanning machines that measured their alertness. This ranged from fully alert, to relaxed, drowsy, and all the way to very sleepy. The results confirmed that time appears to slow down when alertness levels are high. The faster the brainwaves, the higher the alertness level, and the faster information is processed which stretches time intervals, hence, the slower time passes [47]. In contrast, when the participants were less alert, their brainwaves were slow and time passed quickly. This is evident from several typical every day experiences. Let us look at a few examples.

If you have taken a long trip, say an eight-hour flight from Paris to New York, you might have noticed that not all hours feel the same. The first hour is agonizingly slow because you are still quite alert. The next six hours pass more quickly and the time goes faster and faster, as you get tired and less alert. However, in the last hour, as you near your destination, excitement builds up and you become alert once again, so time slows down. Another example is a good night's sleep of eight hours, which might sometimes feel like a few seconds. This is because, during sleep, EEG brainwaves are very slow, alertness and attention are mostly shut down, and sensory input to the brain is minimal, so the brain does not process or 'record' much information. When you wake up, you recall very few mental snapshots of the whole night, which gives the impression that it only lasted for a few moments as if time flew, when you might have been actually sleeping for eight hours.

'The more alert we are, the slower time seems to run and vice versa'

We normally descend into sleep in several stages that repeat continuously, and are characterized by decreasing EEG brainwave frequencies. The brainwaves of 4 – 8 Hz dominate the first drowsy stage, followed by moderate-to-deep sleep having brainwaves ranging from 2 – 4 Hz and, finally, the deepest sleep state which has the slowest brainwaves of 0.5 -2 Hz, and from which it is very difficult to wake people up. The entire sequence usually takes about an hour and is called non-rapid eye movement sleep (non-REM). During these stages, brainwaves continue to slow down, alertness decreases, and so sleeping time passes very quickly. Once the deepest level of sleep is reached, the sequence reverses itself and brainwaves start to speed up to reach a state called the rapid eye movement sleep, or REM. In REM sleep, the EEG recordings are characterized by faster brainwaves (15 – 60 Hz) that are remarkably similar to those when we are fully alert and awake. This is when most dreams occur and the faster brainwaves in this stage are the reason why a one-minute dream sometimes feels like an hour to the dreamer. However, this REM state only lasts about 10 minutes and the brain cycles back into the non-REM sleep stages. Each night, we experience on average 4 cycles of REM sleep, each having longer and longer durations. The overall effect is that we wake up and feel like the whole night passed in an instant, except for the duration of a few dreams that seemed longer than usual.

The same effect is observed, but to a lesser extent, in daydreaming. When you allow your imagination to wander freely, you are no longer fully aware of what is going on around you, and you quickly lose track of time. During that state, the brainwaves' frequency declines to the range of 3 to 8 Hz where alertness is low and the brain's 'recording' speed is slow, causing time to fly. Daydreaming is probably the most popular way of speeding up time when one has to attend a boring meeting or sit through an uninspiring lesson at school!

People report a similar effect when under hypnosis. Hypnotized people are known to underestimate the duration for which they were under hypnosis by as much as 40 per cent [48]. The brain does not process much information under hypnosis, so 20 minutes might seem like just 12 minutes when it is time to wake up. However, sometimes people can be tricked into believing that time has been stretched. That is because hypnosis is very similar to the REM dream state, which resembles the awake state. In one experiment, hypnotized people were told to imagine that they were preparing a very complicated meal and had one hour to perform that task but, in reality, were only given 10 seconds. After those 10 seconds had elapsed in real world time, the hypnotized subjects were awakened and the reported experiencing intricate and accurate details in their inner perception that seemed like a full hour!

Moving further down the scale of alertness is the state of anesthesia. A general anesthetic that is given during surgery has an even more pronounced effect on time. The drug decreases the firing rate of brain neurons immensely and the brain's processing speed approaches zero as the patient loses consciousness and is put into deep sleep. The brain's 'video camera' is essentially turned off. Anyone who has undergone surgery will tell you that when he or she woke up, it felt as though no time had passed at all. A similar situation occurs with people who go into a state of coma for years and wake up feeling that time has frozen, as if they were only gone for an instant. In such states, alertness is almost null, the brain's information processing speed approaches zero, and the experienced speed of time runs extremely fast.

It is easy to see that as the levels of alertness drop, from fully awake to deep sleep, the brain's information processing speed declines and, with it, time subjectively speeds up. Now what about situations where alertness levels increase? Let us look at some examples that slow down time.

The Oddball Effect

When we are fully awake, the speed of time runs at the normal speed that we are used to during an average day. In such an awake state, our brainwaves fluctuate in the range of 8 to 13 Hz when we are calm and relaxed. These are the strongest and most prominent electrical activity in the awake human brain and average 10 Hz that is one cycle every 100 milliseconds. We already saw how that time interval is important to our perception of reality and normal experience of time. However, when we are engaged in focused mental activity, problem solving, and decision making, we are usually more alert and the brainwaves speed up to the range of 13 to 38 Hz. This can go up to 70 Hz when we are hyper-alert, super focused, and processing information in different areas of the brain simultaneously. When we are in such a state, our brains absorb so much information each second, like the slo-mo high recording speed on a smartphone, that we feel time is running slowly. We saw in the beginning of this chapter how people that produce high frequency brainwaves, such as great athletes, artists, thinkers, also tend to have high levels of intelligence, alertness, and a higher perception of reality, i.e. a more sensitive sense of hearing, vision, smell and taste. Their brains are capable of processing large amounts of information in very short periods of time, as if time is running in slow motion in their mind.

Evidence for how an increase in alertness slows down the time experience comes from a well-known phenomenon called the 'Oddball Effect'. This occurs when the brain experiences something unusual or out of the normal order of events, causing it to suddenly become more alert. It can be illustrated in a simple experiment. A person sitting in front of a computer screen is repeatedly shown an image of, say, a zebra for one second each time. After seeing the same zebra ten times, a novel 'oddball' image of a flower is presented for the same duration of one second. The person is later asked how long the 'oddball' flower image was shown for, and most people would judge it to have lasted for longer than the repetitive zebra image, even though both lasted exactly one second. The main reason for this effect is that the brain pays special attention and spends more time processing odd events, recording as much information as possible of the novel circumstances. After observing the zebra image a few times, it starts to barely make an impression and the brain is no longer interested in processing any further information. But suddenly the 'oddball' flower image appears, the brain becomes more alert, starts processing more information, and so is tricked into believing that it lasted longer than the repetitive images [49]. This boost in alertness directed at odd events leads to a feeling that time has slowed down. The only difference between the two is the alertness and degree of attention the brain has devoted to each image.

In another interesting study, researchers tested participants who attended an annual fair in Leuven, Belgium, to see how their mental arousal levels affected time experience, during various roller coaster rides. The researchers chose four different rides with varying degrees of excitement and alertness ranging from very calm, and relaxed to very active, tense or aroused. They then asked the participants to estimate the rides' durations. The results showed that those who took the most exciting and action-packed rides felt their duration to be longer than they actually were, as if time had slowed down. Whereas those who took the easy-going rides felt shorter ride durations, as if time flew. These findings indicate that action-packed rides cause an increase in the brain's alertness level and information processing speed, which, as we saw, slows down the perceived speed of time [50].

Music, Alertness and the Speed of Time

Listening intently to complex music can halt the flow of time altogether. This is because it involves anticipation, tracking what is going on in the song, and predicting what will come next. All these tasks require focused attention and higher information processing speeds that stretch the experienced duration of listening to music. A couple of decades ago, psychologist, Frances Rauscher, and her colleagues made headlines by discovering that listening to Mozart can improve people's mathematical skills and spatial reasoning. A two-year study of 1,200 children in Switzerland found that those who were given extra music lessons performed better than those who were not. Teaching those children more music at school improved their ability to learn language and social skills [51]. Researchers also showed that even rats can run mazes faster after hearing Mozart! However, these 'musical' effects are not limited to those mental functions but extend to time perception as well. It is now known that music, not just classical, raises our alertness levels by causing a large amount of dopamine neurotransmitters to be released inside the brain. Listening to music also significantly increases blood flow to the brain and reduces blood pressure [52]. This kind of aural stimulation excites the brain and causes it to process more information than usual. This was confirmed in a study from the Stanford University of Medicine where people were given special headphones through which to listen to music while getting their brains scanned using a functional magnetic resonance imaging (fMRI) machine. The research team found that music caused certain areas in the brain responsible for paying attention, alertness, mental arousal, and planning, to light up. The boost in alertness results in faster thinking, which implies a fast ticking internal clock that stretches the experienced durations. It explains why listening to a nice song intently stretches its duration [53].

Music also hijacks our sense of time. It flows at a certain rhythm, creating a sequence of time units that do not typically align with our internal clock, and distorting our experienced speed of time. This music time creates a parallel time reality that steals our connection to objective real time. Experiments have shown that just listening to fast repetitive sound clicks is enough to speed up our internal clock. The highly-structured and almost mathematical music of Mozart is perfect for this effect [54]. In 2004, the Royal Automobile Club Foundation for Motoring suggested that Wagner's *Ride of the Valkyrie*, is the most dangerous music to listen to while driving. The reason is not so much the distraction but the fact that Wagner's furiously fast tempo challenges the driver's normal sense of time causing their internal clock to speed up and time intervals to stretch. The tendency to accelerate the car will then seem less risky, putting them in potentially life-threatening danger.

Another interesting study on the effect of music was conducted by marketing expert, James Kellaris, who investigated the influence of music on waiting queues in shopping malls and consumer environments. He found that people who had enjoyed a nice piece of music, when asked to estimate its duration, felt it had lasted longer compared to music they did not like [55]. Marketing research has shown that people spend 38 percent more time in supermarkets when the background music is slow. It is also known that more drinks are sold in bars when slow tempo music is played. Moreover, Dr. Kellaris found that loud music created the illusion of slower time as well [56]. This is because louder music draws more attention and makes people more alert compared to softer music. The louder the song, the higher the mental arousal and the longer the song's duration seems. This is important for restaurant operators, for instance, who know that the longer a customer has to wait for service, the less satisfied he will be. Consequently, if loud music is playing, it will expand the consumer's perception of the time spent waiting and his negative experience will be amplified. Interestingly, this effect is more pronounced in females because they generally perceive music to be louder than males due to their more sensitive hearing ability, particularly at the higher frequency range of 4,000 Hz and above. So now you understand why your wife tends to get over-irritated when a waiter delays serving your dinner; loud music playing in the restaurant background is probably the culprit!

Let us now look at some examples where the brain experiences a short burst of extreme alertness, and high processing power that can almost 'freeze' time; situations that make roller coaster rides look like a walk in the park.

Extreme Alertness: Experiencing 'Bullet Time'

Imagine driving back home after a long day at work when a car suddenly strays from its lane and comes straight at you on a direct collision path. Your alertness gets a sudden boost and your brain starts recording everything: every detail, every movement, every adjacent car, every thought, and every bit of information that might be useful for your survival. As a result, your brain processes a huge amount of mental snapshots in a very short period of time. In a normal situation, it would take a longer period of time to record the same amount of information, in comparison. But when you later recall those rich memories, you will feel that the event was longer as if time was going in slow motion.

People involved in life-threatening situations often report time as having slowed down. When someone is involved in a seriously dangerous situation, they will experience extreme levels of fear that elevate their alertness to abnormal levels. A person standing at the side of the road observing a car crash accident would barely measure a fraction of a second for the whole incident, whereas the driver going through the crash will later recall it as passing in slow motion. He can often describe the tiniest details of the collision and would swear that the event was several seconds long as if "time stood still". In movies, such as *Kill Bill*, action-packed scenes are often shown in slow motion 'bullet time' to portray what the character is subjectively experiencing in those thrilling moments! In extreme cases, people on their death beds often report their whole life flashing before their eyes in a matter of seconds. It is possible that their brain goes into some kind of turbo hyper-alert mode in its final moments and time appears to slow down to the extent that an entire lifetime can be replayed once again in those last few seconds!

'People involved in life-threatening situations often report time as having slowed down'

The first detailed description of extreme life-threatening experiences comes from a distinguished late nineteenth century professor of geology named Albert von St. Gallen Heim. Heim had fallen while climbing in the Alps and experienced a near-death experience himself. Following his own experience, he spent 25 years collecting numerous accounts of people who had had similar accidents, and lived to tell the tale. In his interviews that he recorded in the 1892 *Yearbook of the Swiss Alpine Club*, he noted how around 95% of the climbers who had an accidental fall had experienced time going in slow motion [57]. This was similar to his own experience in which "time became greatly expanded" as his body dropped towards the ground. All survivors mentioned experiencing a high level of alertness and clarity of mind, enabling them to react quickly in the face of danger. A 19-year-old climber reported, for instance, that during his fall, the fear and hope of survival "forced a concentration of my thoughts on rescue efforts and a redirection of my whole mind onto whatever might be necessary to prevent the potential plunge" [58]. Incidentally, Albert Heim also happened to be one of Albert Einstein's professors, who might have possibly influenced Einstein's thinking that time and space are not fixed and constant, but change with motion. Heim's experience that "As an object hurtles through space, time is altered relative to motion and speed", may have inspired Einstein's 'Theory of Relativity'.

Likewise, jet pilots who were ejected from their planes in the Vietnam War, confirm similar experiences of time slowing down. In one interview, a jet pilot described "... when the nose-wheel strut collapsed I vividly recalled, in a matter of about 3 seconds, over a dozen actions necessary for successful recovery of flight altitude. The procedures I needed were readily available. I had almost total recall and felt in complete control." In another interview, a pilot recounts, "As soon as we were airborne, the aircraft started to roll to the left. Time was expanded greatly, so it felt like several minutes before it was time to get out... I assumed ejection posture and pulled the lower handle. Again, there was time expansion. The canopy leaving, the seat going up the rail, and the aircraft disappearing below me seemed to take several minutes. Only a few seconds later, my feet hit the ground... Just as immediate, I was surrounded by people asking how I was, and the one-and-a-half-minute ordeal that took ten minutes was over." In similar interviews, a 14-year-old boy who had accidentally shot himself in the chest reported that his "thoughts were speeded up and time seemed stretched out" [57].

The common aspects that are often reported in these dangerous situations are mental quickness and increased speed of thoughts, unusually sharp vision or hearing, high level of alertness and focus on issues relevant to survival. Almost all people report a feeling that time slowed down to a great extent, resulting in the perception that the event lasted longer than it actually did. A faster information processing speed means the internal clock speeds up, and the flow of time is slower, thus giving the person more time to plan their next move. Another key ingredient in those life-threatening situations is the element of surprise. This is evident from hospital patients who are similarly facing life-threatening terminal illnesses, yet do not experience an increased speed of thought or enhanced alertness. Nor do they experience a slowing of the speed of time.

To empirically test this time distortion effect, researchers took 76 novice sky divers, who were undertaking their first skydive, into a plane flying at 14,000 feet. They then measured their fear and stress levels before the skydive and after landing. They also asked them to estimate how long they thought the experience lasted. They found that time appeared to pass more slowly in direct proportion to increase in the level of fear [59]. In another interesting experiment, Dr. David Eagleman wrapped a special chronometer device around participants' wrists and made them jump from a 31 meter high platform into a safety net to see if they could distinguish very short time intervals when in danger. The results showed that participants felt their free-fall time was, on average, 36% longer than it actually was. This implied that the intense emotional experience of the free fall must have enhanced their alertness and caused them to capture richer memories during the fall, leading to the perception that time slowed down [60].

Fight or Flight: It is Wired into our Brains

The instinctive reaction that increases our alertness in response to danger is believed to be a natural product of our evolutionary history. Our ancestors' brains developed a mechanism that enhanced our ability to make quick decisions in moments crucial to our survival. Psychologists call it the 'fight or flight' mode. When in danger, the whole body goes into action. The heart beat rate rises to pump more blood to the brain. Fat is released into the blood to provide that extra energy for the muscles. Sweat is secreted from the skin to provide further cooling if needed, and the brain is flushed with neurotransmitters that enhance the neurons firing rate and information processing speed, to ensure that critical data is captured so that vital decisions can be made. Quick reactions and decisions made in a split second make all the difference between life and death!

When going through a near-death experience, such as the climbers' free fall, the 'flight or fight' mode is activated. The brain's concentration and attention levels rise dramatically causing neurotransmitter levels, like dopamine, to surge suddenly. This boosts the brain's information processing speed, or 'speed of thoughts', and the brain starts absorbing and recording a huge amount of information in a very short period of time. If the brain normally captures around 10 snapshots every second under relaxed conditions, during an accident, the high level of attention might cause the brain to capture, say, 50 snapshots in just one second. Under normal circumstances, the brain would require 5 seconds to capture those 50 mental snapshots. When those dense and rich memories are recalled, the brain assumes that these snapshots must have been captured over a period of 5 seconds, instead of the one second it actually took to capture them. Therefore, one 'real' second in a life-threatening situation would appear to have been stretched to 5 seconds of 'perceived' subjective time, and explains why such events appear to run in slow motion.

Great athletes all have the ability to slow down time by inducing the same kind of focus and concentration produced in life-threatening situations. The only difference is that they can do it at will, i.e. without having to go through the experience of a mountain free fall or a car crash. Having an alertness and focused attention like that of great sports stars is not impossible to achieve. To succeed, it is important to maintain a healthy brain that enhances our innate level of alertness, so that we can slow down time and makes our days last longer. Here are three practical tips.

Boosting Alertness with Sleep and Exercise

It is obvious that one way of enhancing alertness is by getting enough sleep. Depriving yourself of adequate sleep does some awful things to your brain. Your ability to plan, learn, concentrate, solve problems, and stay alert is affected. Researchers estimate that if you have been awake for 21 hours straight, your mental ability is equivalent to someone who is legally drunk! The same effect can occur if you had a couple of late nights followed by early mornings [61]. You will be sleepy most of the following day and time will run so fast so that day will be over before you know it. Fortunately, the effects of sleep deprivation are reversible. An extra hour or two of sleep can enhance your performance on tasks that require sustained attention. So never underestimate the power of a good night's sleep.

When you force your brain to concentrate for a few hours non-stop, you start losing processing power and your attention levels drop, so time starts to speed up. A quick break or power nap in between can reboot your alertness and replenish your energy levels. The ideal time is between 1:00 and 3:00 p.m. since the body naturally experiences a dip in energy around that period. A nap around that time, as short as 10 minutes but not more than 30 minutes, can restore alertness, and help in slowing down that afternoon. Naps are also the best way to travel painlessly through time into the future, as duly noted by Carlyle, the quintessential kitten in the comic strip Kit and Carlyle!

Contrary to popular belief, napping at work is not for lazy people. Winston Churchill, Albert Einstein, and Bill Clinton were famous nap-takers. In Japan, more and more companies are encouraging employees to sleep on the job. There are even cafes and massage parlors which offer napping services. Companies like Google and Nike have a number of quiet rooms or napping pods around their campus. The same goes for airline companies. A quick catnap is even better than a cup of coffee because caffeine, even though it enhances alertness, can decrease memory performance, meaning you are prone to making mistakes. This trend is gaining momentum as companies realize how costly it is in terms of reduced productivity, errors, and accidents when their employees are sleep-deprived. Power naps are supported by a wealth of research that shows that they improve alertness, learning, and cognition [62]. A study by the U.S. space agency NASA reveals that jet pilots who take a short nap increase their performance by as much as 34 per cent and enhance their alertness by 100 per cent [63]. Therefore, to maintain an alert brain that slows down time throughout the day, it is essential that you get at least 7 to 8 hours of sleep every night and have a quick power nap when your concentration levels decline.

Physical exercise has also been shown to increase mental arousal and alertness levels which are a key factor in slowing the passage of time [64]. Even mild exercise can boosts alertness levels by facilitating an adequate constant flow of oxygen to the brain. When the brain is not properly oxygenated, you start losing concentration. The action of gravity tends to keep blood in the lower part of your body and, as a result, you become less alert. That is why it is important to get up and take a walk every hour or so to get the blood pumping and oxygenate the brain.

One interesting study found that even chewing gum, which is a very mild physical activity, can improve oxygen and blood circulation to the brain and can boost reaction time and alertness by around 10 per cent [65]. Japanese researchers using fMRI to scan the brains of volunteers that performed a mental test on a computer screen while chewing gum found that as many as eight areas of the brain were lit up by the simple act of chewing. These are the same brain areas involved in mental arousal, alertness, and psychomotor skills, and explain why chewing gum improves mental performance. Therefore, remember next time you are having a good time and want that to last longer, chewing a gum to boost your alertness can go a long way in slowing down that time experience!

Diet for an Alert Brain

We are all very careful in choosing a balanced diet that keeps us healthy, whether it is fish for the heart, bananas for the digestive system, reduced sugar content to prevent diabetes, and anti-oxidants for fighting potential cancers. What about food for the brain? What kind of diet can enhance our alertness so that our brains are capable of recording more of the world around us? Are there any food supplements or nutrients that be used to increase the brain's processing speed so it captures more mental snapshots and slow the passage of time?

You are what you eat. What you eat affects how you think. And how you think affects how you experience time. A healthy brain diet is important for maintaining a sharp and alert brain. The type of diet you give to your brain can affect your mental clarity, temperament, and memory, all of which can considerably affect your alertness level and your perceived speed of time. A diet that contains brain *superfoods* such as blueberries, dark chocolate, green tea, oily fish, and plenty of water is essential for providing the building blocks the body needs to produce important neurotransmitters, which, as you will recall, are the brain's chemical messengers. Brain health is outside the scope of this book, but I would strongly recommend reading books such as *Change Your Brain, Change Your Life* by Dr. Daniel G. Amen, or *Your Creative Brain* by Shelley Carson, *Boost Your Brain: The New Art and Science Behind Enhanced Brain Performance* by Dr. Majid Fotuhi and Christina Antoniadis. I also offer a free guide to a Healthy Brain Diet that you can download from my website (see details at the end of the book). These brain diets are essential for maintaining the kind of alert brain that can slow down time.

**'You are what you eat. What you eat affects how you think.
And how you think affects how you experience time'**

Recap

To sum up, the speed at which our brain records reality depends on our ability to sustain focused attention and stay alert. The more alert we are, the faster we can process sensory information and the slower time appears to pass. This is evident from great athletes, the 'oddball effect', and the way time appears in slow motion when going through life-threatening situations. Listening to good music also slows down time. Conversely, time speeds up when we are less alert, such as in the state of daydreaming, drowsy, or going through the deeper levels of sleep. Therefore, when you are in a situation that you really need to speed up, a quick trip to dreamland should do the trick!

In the next chapter, we will explore the role of emotions on how we perceive time. Our emotions can be a powerful factor in shaping our perception of the speed of time. Therefore, it is important to understand what can be done to control their influence.

CHAPTER 7

TAKING CONTROL

THE EFFECT OF EMOTIONS

'From time sadness borrows wings'
— La Fontaine

'A day without laughter is a day wasted'
— Charlie Chaplin

Classifying Emotions

Emotions play a powerful role in distorting our time perception. They dictate our experienced speed of time. Negative emotions such as fear, anger, anxiety, and sadness appear to slow down the passage of time so that we feel we must endure these feelings for longer than we actually do, making the negative experience even worse. It is, therefore, important to understand how that happens and what can be done to shorten the perceived duration of unpleasant feelings and prolong the duration of pleasant ones. Let us start with an exploration of how long emotions really last.

In contrast to moods, the actual durations of emotions are generally well-defined. They start with an internal or external trigger and end when the intensity of the emotional experience subsides and there is a return to the initial baseline level of emotion. Emotions can last anywhere from a couple of seconds for up to several hours, whereas moods last relatively longer and are not as intense. Sadness is considered the longest-lasting emotion. In a 2014 study, high-school students in Belgium were requested to recall recent emotional incidents and report their durations. They had to fill in questionnaires about recent episodes of the emotion in question and briefly describe the emotion-triggering event. They then had to rate the duration and intensity of that emotion and how it affected them. The researchers found that, out of a total of 27 reported emotions, sadness lasted the longest, whereas shame, surprise, fear, and disgust quickly faded away [66]. The main reason is that sadness is almost always associated with very important events such as deaths or accidents that have a great impact on our lives. The implications of such events take time to digest and we tend to rethink the consequences repeatedly in our minds. This, in turn, causes the sad emotions to be strengthened and sustained over a longer period of time. In contrast, emotions such as shame, disgust, and fear are generally the result of involuntary reactions that, though they can be incredibly powerful, are often over in a flash. This obviously does not preclude the fact that fear, in certain situations of domestic abuse, or even shame (such as felt by anorexics) can also last very long.

Most psychologists agree that emotions can be defined by two main attributes: the intensity of the emotion and its valence- that is, how pleasant or unpleasant it is. Thus, emotions can be broadly classified into 4 main groups:

1. High intensity and unpleasant, such as fear, anger, and anxiety
2. High intensity and pleasant, such as love, passion, and awe
3. Low intensity and unpleasant, such as shame, guilt, sadness, and disgust
4. Low intensity but pleasant, such as satisfaction, pride, and hope

'Our emotions dictate the experienced speed of time'

How Emotions Affect Time Perception

Over the last 10 years, researchers have started to systematically investigate the mechanisms involved in time distortions that occur in the presence of various emotions. In typical experiments participants are shown high-intensity pleasant images, such as erotic scenes, while other participants are shown high-intensity unpleasant images, such as a gruesome murder scene. Both sets of images are displayed for the same length of time, but those who watch the pleasant images report shorter durations, as if time was running fast, while those who see the unpleasant images report longer durations, as if time has slowed down.

Researchers have, similarly, investigated the effect of emotional sounds on time perception. In a 2007 study from *Laboratoire de Neurosciences Cognitives* in Paris, four groups of sounds were used: (a) pleasant high-intensity sounds, e.g. erotic sounds, (b) pleasant low-intensity sounds, e.g. laughs, (c) unpleasant low-intensity sounds, e.g. sobs, and (d) unpleasant high-intensity sounds, e.g. a woman crying or wailing. There was also one group of neutral sounds, e.g. street noises. The results confirmed that emotionally unpleasant sounds were perceived to be longer than pleasant or neutral sounds. The rational explanation behind this effect is that we tend to focus more attention on negative emotions than on positive ones. This activates our central nervous system, speeds up information processing, and accelerates the mechanisms that support our brain's internal clock. A faster ticking internal clock, as we know, leads to an expansion of time intervals, so it feels as if time is running slowly [67].

Another possible explanation has to do with a particular area in the brain called the *anterior insular cortex*, which is the size of a prune, folded and tucked deep within the cerebral cortex. This area 'lights up' if you try to guess the time while inside an fMRI machine that is scanning your brain. It so happens that this region of the brain is also responsible for processing our own bodily sensations. One can therefore conclude that the experience of time is possibly related to the amount of stimulation our brains receive from our body, or our level of self-awareness, not just the sensory information received from the external world. Self-awareness is only possible as an entity across time. Since emotions tend to draw our attention to ourselves, when we are experiencing an emotional moment, we become more aware of our own body, which simulates the insular cortex and our perception is that time slows down. In contrast, when we are absorbed with an activity, like watching an action movie or reading an interesting book that distracts us from our own self, time seems to fly. Attention to time, such as in waiting or boring situations, draws awareness to our own self causing time to drag. The greater our self-awareness, such as when we are sad or anxious, the slower time passes and vice versa. So are there any counter-measures we can take to speed up time when we are feeling bad?

The Effect of Taking Control

Before we look at each of the main unpleasant emotions in detail, you will note that one common aspect in all countermeasures is the need to take control of our emotions. Only by taking control do we nullify the time-expanding effects of these negative emotions. In fact, researchers have demonstrated that the stretching effect of perceived time can be corrected by simply making a person feel that he is in control [68]. In 2012, at the University of Illinois, Dr. Buetti and Dr. Lleras conducted a series of experiments with participants that were shown positive and negative images on a computer monitor and were requested to estimate the time duration of each image. As expected, the participants consistently *over-estimated* the duration of negative images, as if time slowed down and *under-estimated* the duration of positive ones, as if time flew. But then the researchers introduced the illusion of control by telling participants that they could press a button on the keyboard to increase the number of positive and decrease the number of negative images that appeared on the screen, if they felt the need. Behind the scenes, however, it was the researchers who were actually controlling the number of positive or negative images that they were seeing. For some participants, the researchers followed the participants' wishes in order to give them the illusion that they were in control. But for others, they did the opposite, making the participants feel that they had no control at all over how often positive or negative images appeared. When the participants were later asked to estimate the duration of the images, the researchers noted that the lengthening or shortening of time intervals was more or less neutralized for the participants who had the illusion of control. The conclusion was that when participants were allowed to believe they were in control, the time expansion caused by their emotions was eliminated!

An important practical conclusion to take from this result is that in order to neutralize the time-stretching effect of fear, anger, anxiety, or sadness, you need to convince yourself that you are in control. This is essential if you want to shorten the amount of time for which you have to endure these negative feelings. What follows are a few practical tips that will help you do just that.

When you Feel Fear

We saw in the previous chapter how time seems to pass in slow motion for people experiencing extreme fear in life-threatening situations. Time appears to slow down in direct proportion to the amount of fear induced by the situation. In 2011, psychologists Sylvie Droit-Volet and Sandrine Gil gathered a group of psychology students at the University of Blaise, in France, to study how emotions resulting from watching certain movies affected their sense of time [69]. One group of students was shown extracts from movies that are known to induce fear (such as *The Blair Witch Project*, *Scream*, and *The Shining*), and another was shown extracts from sad movies (such as *City of Angels*, *Philadelphia* or *Dangerous Minds*). A third group was shown "neutral" video clips (like weather forecasts or stock market updates). The researchers then asked the students to estimate the duration of the movie extracts. They found that fear distorted time perception the most. Students who watched the horror movies felt that scenes were much longer than they really were while the sad and neutral movies had little effect. In a similar study at Saint Joseph's College of Maine in 2007, students were shown one of two video clips; one clip was taken from the news coverage of the September 11 2001 terrorist attacks, and the other clip was a non-stressful familiar scene from *The Wizard of Oz*. Even though both clips were exactly 3 minutes long, students who watched the stressful September 11th footage estimated its duration to be much longer compared to the non-stressful Oz clip [70].

To watch a scary movie is one thing, but to actually experience real fear is something else. Back in 1961, researchers at Clark University, Massachusetts, blindfolded some students and asked them to walk on a high platform towards a drop, towards danger, while other students were requested to walk away from it, towards safety. The results showed that the students who were in danger tended to over-estimate the duration of that walk compared to the students who were walking towards safety [71]. Furthermore, some students were asked to stop and wait at 15 feet from the drop. They felt that time passed slower than those who were asked to stop at a much safer distance. The fear of imminent danger caused the waiting time interval to stretch. In a similar study, arachnophobic participants who spent one minute watching a spider judged that duration to be longer compared to non-arachnophobic participants. Time seemed to slow down in direct proportion to their fear of spiders [72].

Fear has been shown to be one of the most intense emotions. It causes physical responses such as dilated pupils, increased blood pressure, accelerated heartbeat, release of adrenalin, and a surge in alertness levels. These reactions form the basis of our 'fight or flight' instinct, the defensive mechanism that we saw earlier. When we experience fear, the heightened level of alertness causes the brain's information processing speed to rise dramatically so that the brain can make the best-informed decision. When those memories are recalled, they appear to have taken longer to capture. In other words, fear causes the brain's internal clock to speed up so you can react faster. This leads to the stretching of time intervals, and hence the perception of a 'slowing down' of time. And that is a useful thing for short bursts of fear, such as in a fist fight or when under attack by an animal. It is only when fear is constant that the time-distorting effect becomes substantial to affect people's lives. So what can we do to shorten the duration of these negative emotions?

'Time appears to slow down in direct proportion to the amount of fear induced'

Psychologists all agree that the best ways to deal with fear is to first acknowledge and define it. Is it a fear of people? Fear of public speaking?

Fear of heights? Fear of germs or fear of public spaces? Fear of planes? Or maybe it is fear of death, as Woody Allen once notably said: "I'm not afraid of death; I just don't want to be there when it happens!" It might not be easy to name because it might be a mixture of other emotions like anxiety or shame. But defining and understanding what kind of fear is crucial to gaining control over it. It is also recommended to scrutinize it and find out how it began. Was it a negative experience from the past? Is it something that occurred in childhood? What triggers that fear? This is all easier said than done, of course, and, in many cases, overcoming fear requires the support of a psychiatrist. However, research has shown that one of the most effective ways to overcome fears is to confront them. Recall that our instinctive reaction to fear is 'fight', 'flight', or 'freeze'. That is the way our brains have been wired throughout millions of years of evolution. If something looks weaker than us, we fight it. If it looks stronger but slower, we run. If it is stronger and faster, there is not much we can do but freeze and hope it does not see us! These are the typical reactions we normally experience when we face fear. To conquer our fears, freezing and running away will not work. The best way is to confront them head-on and expose ourselves to small doses to help us to overcome them bit by bit. This relates back to the benefits of taking control that we just saw earlier. It is also important to surround ourselves with people who encourage us and help us overcome our fears. As we shall see shortly, the people we spend the most time with affect our emotional state and thus the perceived speed of time.

When you are Angry

The American Psychological Association defines anger as "a reaction to a perceived threat to ourselves, our loved ones, our property, our self-image, or some part of our identity." Its intensity varies widely from mild irritation and frustration, to extreme rage. Anger produces physical reactions, starting with a rush of adrenaline, increased heart rate and blood pressure, and tightening of muscles. These reactions increase alertness levels and influence the way we experience time.

The effect of anger on our time perception is similar to fear; it slows it down. This is consistent with studies showing that anger and fear are both highly intense and unpleasant emotions. In one study, psychologist Sylvie Droit-Volet showed students images of four different facial expressions: angry, fearful, happy, and a neutral face, and requested them to estimate how long the image was shown for. The duration of angry facial expressions being shown was consistently over-estimated when compared to happy faces [73]. The same effect was confirmed in 2007 at the University of Blaise Pascal, France, when children, 3 to 8 years old, were shown angry and neutral female faces. They tended to judge the duration of angry faces to be longer than that of neutral faces. This effect is, therefore, a natural inborn instinct and not something we learn when we grow up [74]. The reason for this effect has to do, again, with our evolutionary history and built-in defense mechanism. Angry faces indicate an intent to attack and are more closely linked to human survival than any other expression. You normally feel anger in response to a perceived threat or grievance that you blame on someone or something. Anger drives you to focus your attention on that threat and to take action against it in order to regain control. This increase in alertness leads to a rise in the information processing speed, which is crucial for anticipating danger and preparing to act quickly. The result is an expansion of time intervals and the perception that time is passing slowly. So what can we do about it? How can we shorten a period of anger?

Well, we cannot completely eliminate or avoid the things or the people that enrage us. Nor can we change them, at least not all the time, but we can learn to control our reactions. This is not to say that anger can sometimes be useful in some situations, such as in response to being treated badly as an employee – as long as it is funneled into a constructive response. But anger generally needs to be controlled because, if left unchecked, it can affect our health and will make unpleasant situations seem longer than they really are. Too much uncontrolled anger will be bottled up inside and end up blowing up one day when you least expect it. If you have seen the comedy movie *Anger Management*, there is a scene where Jack Nicholson tries to explain to Adam Sandler that there are two kinds of angry people in this world: explosive and implosive. The explosive screams at the cashier for not accepting their coupons. The implosive is the cashier who keeps quiet until one day he shoots everyone in the store. We have all heard the advice not to suppress our anger because it might lead to stomach ulcers or heart problems. But this does not mean we should vent our anger by shouting at people or kicking the door. Research has shown that such actions can still have the same negative effect on our health. Anger fires up our 'fight or flight' response and causes our heart to race, our jaw to clench, and our body to release fat from our muscles, just in case we need that extra energy for the fight. If those fats are not used in a fight, they have nowhere to go and end up sticking on our artery walls. Thus every time your blood pressure shoots up, you inflict a small injury to your heart. This should not be a major problem for a healthy heart but if it is repeated, day after day, or if someone already has heart problems, it might lead to a heart attack. In fact, research has shown that healthy people who are angry often are 19% more likely to get a heart attack compared to calmer people [75]. Therefore, anger should be vented in a more constructive way and 'anger management' is one of the best ways to do that. It can help you understand what triggers your angry feelings and how to express them in a healthy and positive way. Taking control is, again, the way to go. Here are a few tips to consider.

When we were kids, we were taught to think before we speak. Research has shown that this is even more important when we are angry. In the heat of the moment, it is easy to say something we will later regret. However, it has been shown that when we breathe slowly, imagine a relaxing scene, or slowly repeat a calming mantra, we give ourselves more time to think. This reduces the heart rate and blood pressure, so that angry feelings subside. It also causes alertness levels and brain processing speed to return to normal levels, so that the internal clock returns to its normal ticking speed, and the time-stretching effect of anger is neutralized. The faster we can get over it, the shorter the duration of that burst of anger will seem. As Ralph Waldo Emerson once said, 'Remember that for every minute you remain angry, you give up sixty seconds of peace of mind'.

When you are Sad

Sadness occurs when we lose something or someone that is important to us. It can range from a simple and brief unhappiness to a long-term grief or sorrow. It must be dealt with or else it can become chronic and lead to depression. Depression is often described as 'gloominess' or 'dejection' and can be devastating. According to the American Psychiatry Association, 'depression is characterized by symptoms of a depressive mood indicated by the feeling of being sad or empty, as well as by a markedly diminished ability to take pleasure in things'. Depression is considered a mood disorder that has a long-lasting duration. It is not a discrete emotion but a mixture of sadness, fear, and anxiety. Important symptoms include a greater desire to be alone, sleeping more than usual, no interest in the usual surroundings, and a loss of appetite. Depressed individuals often feel hopeless; they stop enjoying things and look at the world with a very negative bias.

Let's go back to the experiment which we described earlier, where students were shown horror and drama movies. Researchers, surprisingly, found that students who watched the sad drama movies did not report any major slowing down of time, even though they felt less happy after viewing the drama films. Unlike the emotion of fear, sadness did not alter the perception of time drastically. The reason is that sadness is considered to be a low-intensity emotion that induces a slowing down of mental and motor activity[76]. The strength of a feeling of sadness depends on its cause, such as frustration, grief, or sympathy with others, as well as on its intensity and duration. Only prolonged periods of intense sadness will develop into depression which does have the strength to affect time perception [77]. But the feelings of sadness that are produced by watching drama movies are not considered to be strong enough to affect the brain's physiological functions and its internal clock speed.

On the other hand, profound sadness and depression often results in a feeling that time is passing more slowly than normal. For instance, if patients with depression and non-depressed individuals were requested to wait for 5 minutes, the depressed patients typically perceives the waiting period to be 8 or even 10 minutes long, depending on the intensity of their depression. In a recent study that was conducted on 21 clinically depressed patients, participants were asked to count up to 30 at the rate of one count per second. The results showed that it took them almost 40 seconds to 'produce' the 30-second time interval. The results confirm that depression causes an expansion of time intervals and a slowing down of the experience of time [78]. So what does research say about the best ways to shorten those sad periods?

Psychologists tend to agree that ignoring and trying to fight away sad thoughts is not helpful. The consensus is that expressing sadness helps to exorcise it. But they also confirm that ruminating over sadness for long periods can be emotionally damaging too. It is true that sadness needs time to heal, and psychologists recommend we give it the time it needs, but sadness stretches that time in our mind making it appear longer than it really is. La Fontaine was right when he said 'From time sadness borrows wings' which is sometimes translated "Sadness flies away on the wings of time'. To counter that, psychologists recommend distractions, such as reading a book or going for a walk. It has also been shown that listening to upbeat music, singing, and dancing can create positive vibes that improve overall mood. Socializing is another great distraction so it is very important to connect with close friends in times of sadness. A few interesting studies have also found that volunteering time to charity and helping others in areas that matters to them, can also help in relieving sadness. Making someone smile makes people feel good and cause them to appreciate the good things they have, which puts their sadness in a more positive perspective [79, 80].

When you are Anxious

'Today is the tomorrow you worried about yesterday' wrote Dale Carnegie. The American Psychiatric Association defines anxiety as 'an unpleasant state of inner turmoil, often accompanied by nervous behavior, such as pacing back and forth, complaints, and rumination'. Anxiety is not the same as fear. Fear is a response to a real or perceived immediate threat. Anxiety is the expectation of a future threat. Anxiety is a feeling of worry, an overreaction to a situation that is only subjectively seen as menacing.

When we worry, time seems to slow down [81]. If you are late for an important meeting and traveling with an empty gas tank in your car, one minute on a traffic light signal might seem like an hour. That is the effect of anxiety. Studies done on cancer patients who are mentally distressed and suffering from high anxiety levels confirm that they often feel time crawling slowly [82]. In one study in 2006, inpatients with hematological malignancies were recruited at the University Hospital Großhadern in Munich and received treatment during a period of 6 to 8 weeks. Their level of anxiety was measured using a standard psychological questionnaire (HADS). They were then asked to rate how fast they thought time was passing while in the hospital. The results confirmed that the subjective passage of time was slower when cancer patients were more anxious and reported a lower quality of life.

Social rejection is another form of anxiety and leads to a slower experience of time. In an interesting study conducted at San Diego State University in 2003, undergraduate students were separated into groups of 4 -6 people of the same sex. They had their names written on tags and were allowed to talk to each other for 15 minutes. After 15 minutes, the experimenter led the students to separate rooms, where each participant had to nominate two group members that they would most like to work with. However, instead of using the nominations, the students were randomly assigned to be rejected or accepted. Rejected students were told that no one had picked them while accepted students were told that everyone had picked them. In both cases, they were told that they had to work alone because of the unusual outcome. The task was to estimate two time intervals of 40 and 80 seconds each. The results were clear: the 'rejected' students significantly over-estimated the time interval's duration, in clear contrast to the fairly accurate estimates of the 'accepted' students. This clearly demonstrates that time passes very slowly when someone is anxious and socially rejected [83]. The reason is that anxiety increases the level of attention to the passage of time, making it seem longer than it really is. It also increases self-examination and self-awareness which, as we saw, causes durations to appear longer than they really are. So, how can we shorten those anxious moments?

The key to overcoming anxiety is to understand that it is all in our mind. Anxiety is the anticipation of a future risk that may or may not occur. It is an overreaction to a situation that is perceived to be possibly threatening, an internal rumination about an imaginary menace. When we are anxious about something, our brain is tricked into treating it as real danger and the default reaction to danger, as we saw, is the 'fight or flight' mode. The easy way out is, of course, to run away and this is what we tend to do. We might distract ourselves with something else, like listening to music or checking social media. However, the fact is that these actions can only provide the illusion of safety and not a permanent cure. Therefore, psychologists recommend a more drastic approach and that starts with direct confrontation of the thing you are worried about: the 'fight mode', as we shall see next.

According to psychologists, it helps to realize that most of our anxieties are actually exaggerated worries and not actually dangerous. It also helps to move outside of our comfort zone and expose ourselves to small doses of our anxieties, so as to become less sensitive to their symptoms. For instance, someone that is about to deliver a speech to an auditorium full of experts in a field where they are not very knowledgeable would experience extreme anxiety. However, if they have already delivered 20 similar speeches on a familiar subject, they would certainly be more comfortable and confident. To make anxious time pass quickly, it is therefore useful to take steps to confront anxieties in some of the ways that I have outlined.

Psychologists have found that anxiety feeds and grows on negative self-talk and that depends on whether someone is an optimist or a pessimist by default. If the unspoken thoughts that run through someone's mind are mostly positive, they would see unpleasant situations in a more favorable way and expect the best outcomes to occur, not the worst. However, if the self-talk is mostly negative, they will view most situations in a pessimistic manner. This is why psychologists emphasize the importance of being optimistic in treating anxieties. They also encourage being in the company of positive friends, as this diverts attention from exaggerated worries and helps to ground anxieties more realistically. This leads us to another factor that influences the speed of time: the emotions induced by the people we spend the most time with.

'In order to neutralize the time-stretching effect of fear, anger, anxiety, or sadness, you need to convince yourself that you are in control'

Who do you Spend Time with?

'Tell me the company you keep, and I will tell you who you are'. We have all heard that popular saying before. You might have cheerful, always-smiling friends or more pessimistic gloomy ones. Your friends might be easily irritable, hot-tempered or maybe they are cool, relaxed, and laid-back. They may be the anxious type that worries about the slightest thing, or the calm unconcerned type that takes things in their stride. Unconsciously, the people you spend time with influence the person you eventually become and, as it turns out, the type of people you hang out with also influence the speed of time you experience.

When you are being criticized by your boss, time drags, but it races swiftly when you are on a date with someone you love. In order to understand why this is, we must look at the psychological concept of 'embodied emotion'. This is defined as 'the tendency to automatically mimic and synchronize facial expressions, vocalizations, postures and movements with those of another person'. When you are in the company of another person who is expressing emotions like happiness, sadness, anger, or anxiety, you unconsciously imitate that emotion in your own emotional system because it enables you to tune in and understand their feelings. This sort of emotional intelligence varies widely from one person to another though - some people are extremely sensitive to others emotions (i.e. highly sensitive people) whereas others tend to be self-contained. Regardless, embodied emotions are an essential tool in any meaningful social interaction.

Embodied emotions also include synchronizing talking and walking speed with that of another person. It is a tendency acquired early on when babies learn to match their vocalizations to those of their mothers. In response, mothers talk to their children at the speed that matches their information processing speed. When a youngster spends time with a senior person, who speaks and walks more slowly, the young person's walking and talking speed slows down as well. In a seminal study undertaken in 1996, students in an experimental group at New York University asked to form sentences with words such as 'worried', 'Florida', 'old', 'lonely', 'grey', 'wise', 'stubborn', 'forgetful', 'retired', 'wrinkle', 'bitter', etc., words that are related to the elderly stereotype, while other students in the control group had to use neutral words. When they left the laboratory to reach the elevator, the students primed with the words relating to the elderly walked more slowly than the non-primed students! [84] When you spend time with an elderly person, such as your grandfather or grandmother, you unconsciously mimic their slow movement and your internal clock adapts to their slower speed. In the same way, if you spend time with an anxious person, you unconsciously imitate his or her feelings internally, which causes your internal clock to speed up too and, as we saw, time will feel slower. You will become attuned to what that other person is feeling and your time perception will be distorted accordingly.

The effect of embodied emotions on time experience has been demonstrated in various studies. In one interesting experiment from 1975, female participants gazed for 36 seconds at another person who was either smiling or frowning, and felt that time was moving more slowly when the face was frowning than when it was smiling [85]. This is mainly due to the fact that angry faces will ring alarm bells, warning of a potential threat. You are more alert when you see an angry face and this causes your internal clock to speed up, so more mental snapshots are captured and the duration expands, creating the feeling that time slowed down. On the other hand, when you encounter a smiling face, and it is sincere, the impression you get is that you are being welcomed, invited to come closer. A happy face reflects back on you causing you to relax so you are less alert and therefore less mental snapshots are processed leading to the feeling that time is running faster.

The same holds true for being in the company of sad or depressive people. When we see a sad expression on someone's face, we are sympathetic and assume that the person is in need of help. This alerts us to give assistance and increases our attention, which speeds up our internal clock and results in a slowing down of perceived time. In an interesting study, psychologist Sylvie Droit-Valet and her colleagues inhibited this mimicry process by simply putting a pen in the observers' mouths and freezing their facial expressions. This prevented them from developing any sympathetic feelings that would normally occur when they spontaneously imitate the other person's facial expression. As a result, the time-stretching effect was neutralized, and the internal clock remained steady, regardless of the emotion being perceived in the other [86]. It is the same with people who get a Botox treatment and end up with a 'frozen face'. They have greater difficulty embodying other people's emotional expressions and are less empathetic towards them. As a result, Botox will neutralize the time distortion that is normally experienced when people are unconsciously trying to mimic someone's emotional state!

In summary, in social interactions, we unconsciously imitate other peoples' emotional state and match their pace. Emotions are, therefore, contagious and will directly affect our own time experience, speeding it up or slowing it down depending on the other person's emotional state. Once again, choose your friends wisely!

When you Feel Awe

Emotions that are high in intensity generally speed up our internal clock and slow down time. The feeling of awe is another emotion that creates this effect, but it also enhances the feeling that time is abundant, as we shall see shortly.

Awe is one of those emotions that is hard to describe and is characterized by two main aspects. Firstly, it involves the perception of vastness, which is the sense that one has encountered something unfathomable in size or beauty, like the Grand Canyon, in complexity, like thunderstorms, or involves a personal turning point, like witnessing childbirth. In such cases, the trigger is positive. But awe can also have negative triggers, such as witnessing a devastating tsunami or an earthquake. It might also be triggered when you meet a very famous person or someone with great authority. Awe is also a core feature of mystical experiences. It involves a sense of transcendence of time and space, and unity with the universe, a sensation that cannot be described by words, and a feeling that one has experienced a profound insight into the nature of the universe itself. It can be experienced in an instant or in a lifetime, such as when you ponder on the awesomeness of life.

Awe can also stimulate a need for change in your worldview to accommodate the immense experience. You may change your outlook on life and this will impact the way you perceive the world. This was confirmed in a widely-publicized study in 2011 that found that awe feelings can change one's openness to new experiences and can last for years. Participants were recruited from the local community of Johns Hopkins University School of Medicine in Baltimore, USA, using flyers announcing a study on the effect of magic mushroom (psilocybin) on the state of consciousness. Volunteers, who had never taken a psychedelic drug before, were administered a high dose of psilocybin which caused about two-thirds of them to have deep mystical experiences and feelings of awe [87]. They described the awe experience as life-changing and mind-expanding. They also showed a sustained rise in their openness to new experiences that was even evident more than a year later.

In another 2012 study at the University of Minnesota, researchers evaluated the effect of feelings of awe on time perception to see if those feelings can expand people's perception of time-availability which, in turn, might improve their overall happiness. This is important since we now live in a fast-paced age, where time pressure is a common feature of our daily lives. All students were first given fast mental tasks to prime them and make them feel short of time. The students were then split into four groups and shown videos that either evoked awe or happiness. The awe group was shown a commercial showing inspiring and mentally overwhelming scenes such as waterfalls, whales, and space astronauts, while the happiness group watched a commercial featuring people marching happily through rainbow confetti whilst waving flags and wearing brightly colored clothes and face paint. After viewing the films, all participants who experienced awe feelings felt that time had slowed down and was more plentiful. They agreed with statements like "I have lots of time in which I can get things done" and "Time is expanded". Participants in the happiness group, on the other hand, felt more impatient and agreed with statements like "I am pressed for time," and "Time is constricted".

In a separate room, another group of students were instructed to read a short story about a person who ascended the Eiffel Tower and saw Paris from on high, while other students read a neutral story about ascending an unnamed tower and seeing a plain landscape. They were requested to try and feel as the character in the story would have felt. None of the stories contained the word 'awe'. At the end of the session, the students had to answer questionnaires that assessed their perception of time and willingness to volunteer their time. They were also asked whether they preferred material products or experiential goods. For instance, students had to choose whether they preferred a watch or a Broadway show tickets, a $10 gas card or a $10 movie ticket, a jacket or a restaurant dinner, a scientific calculator or a professional massage. The results were again quite interesting. The awe group felt that time slowed down. This increased time-availability, made them less irritable and more willing to volunteer their time to charities compared to other participants. They also showed a preference for experiences such as movies, dinners, or massages, rather than material products such as a watch, gas card, or jacket, and felt they had a more satisfying life [88].

The great Charles Darwin once noted that "Attention, if sudden and close, graduates into surprise; and this into astonishment; and this into stupefied amazement, akin close to terror." [89] The feeling of intense awe involves surprise, astonishment, and 'stupefied amazement'. These are very close to feelings of terror and fear which requires a high level of alertness. Moreover, awe causes people to focus on the present moment and on what is unfolding in front of them. Such intense focus increases the brain's internal clock speed and results in the slowdown of time experience. Therefore, the next time you are under time pressure and feel you are unable to complete things on time, slow down time by experiencing awe. Take a hike in nature and live the moment. Any activity that involves nature such as picnics, hiking, or mountain climbing can induce feelings of awe and significantly stretch a day. Natural time is not measured in seconds or minutes but, rather, in sunrises and sunsets and in the change of seasons. Time is embedded in the natural scenery and moves at such a grand scale that it cannot be contained by simple ticking clocks. When we connect with nature and experience such an imposing expansion of time, we feel a slower pace of time flow that can last for days and even weeks.

Recap

In summary, the various emotions that we might feel during the day have different effects on our time perception. Fear, anger, anxiety, and sadness all slow down the apparent passage of time causing us to endure them for longer than we have to. The key to counter that effect is to believe you are in control. The apparent speed of time also depends on the people you are with and how they make you feel. We may be powerless in controlling the actual duration of our negative emotions, but we have covered a few tips that we can use to shorten their perceived duration. Feelings of awe also expand our time perception and enhance the feeling that time is plentiful. The good news is that you do not have to visit the Grand Canyon or get involved in some wild religious or spiritual gathering to trigger that emotion. Studies have shown that all you need is simply to relive a moment when you felt awe, read a brief 'awesome' story, or just watch an awe-inspiring video. So when you are down, running out of time, or feel the days are slipping by, sit back and relax, watch the National Geographic channel, or YouTube for those awe-inspiring 60-second video clips. Or simply close your eyes and recall an awesome experience from your past to create the feeling of having abundant time that will last for days!

CHAPTER 8

WHAT KIND OF PERSON ARE YOU?

THE EFFECT OF PERSONALITY TRAITS ON TIME PERCEPTION

'The truth is that everyone is bored, and devotes himself to
cultivating habits'
— Albert Camus, 'The Plague'

The Speed of Thought

Admiral Sir John Franklin (1786 – 1847) was a British Royal Navy officer who led several expeditions to explore the Canadian Arctic. A completely fictitious story of his adventures are recounted in a novel by Sten Nadolny titled *The Discovery of Slowness*, in which Franklin is pictured as attaining unimaginable victories because of a strange quality he possesses, namely his very slow perception. Being slow is not generally seen as a positive thing, but in this fiction story, the author portrays Franklin's achievements as only possible because, being slow, he could unintentionally take his time and wait for the right moment to make the winning move. In one battle, for instance, he carefully notes the angle at which a sniper's shots have been discharged, pinpoints his location, and takes him down in one shot from the top of an enemy warship mast. Now, regardless of whether Franklin was really slow or not, the reason I bring up his story here is that his teacher, an 18th century scientist named Dr. Orme, had invented a device to measure the speed at which people perceive the world. The instrument was made up of a disk fastened to a crank on which a man was painted on one side, and a woman painted on the other. When the disk was turned slowly, the man and the woman appeared to follow each other in succession. However, as the disk was turned faster, it reached a speed where the observer could no longer perceive the order in which the man and woman came into view, and started seeing the couple simultaneously hugging each other. Using this device, Dr. Orme could measure people's speed of perception by recording the speed at which the man and woman appeared at the same time. This is similar to the flickering tests (FFF) that measure how fast we can detect flickering lights, which we already saw in chapter 3. Dr. Orme observed that Franklin had a very slow speed of perception and was seeing the couple together when the device was turning at a very slow speed. To borrow a camera metaphor, it was as if he had a very long 'exposure time' so that successive events were perceived as happening simultaneously.

You may have noticed how some people can be fast thinkers and are able to absorb a lot of information in a very short period of time, and how some other are not. In school, for instance, some students are better at understanding what is being taught by the teacher and are fast learners, while others struggle and need things to be repeated a couple of times before they can grasp what is being taught. It is like the idle running speed of a car engine. For an average household car, when the throttle pedal is not pressed, the idle engine would run at 600 rpm. At that speed, the engine generates enough power to run basic functions like the water pump, power steering, and air-conditioning. But for a Formula One race car, the idle running speed of its engine runs at 1,000 rpm. At that speed, the engine can generate more power to perform many more functions. In the same way, some people's brain engines are constantly running in higher-speed mode while others are running at an average innate speed or below.

You can think of it as the innate level of alertness or mental arousal. Now, since the perceived speed of time depends on the speed of perception, it follows that we all experience time differently depending on our brain's engine speed.

You may have encountered gifted and savant children who can perform an amazing number of mathematical calculations in a split second and with relative ease. This is only possible because of their enhanced processing speed that slows the subjective speed of time. Some people can read over 1,000 words per minute, and experience a stretching of time as information flashes through their mind in seconds. Interestingly, studies have also shown that children who have played video games in their childhood are better able to detect fast-flickering lights compared to kids who never played any video games [90]. Flicker fusion, as you recall, is a measure of the brain's information processing speed. Brain scientists confirm that playing video games can almost double a child's intelligence. One study of 491 boys and girls, aged 12 years old, also showed that playing video games increased their creativity substantially [91]. Another study conducted with 3,195 children from six European countries, aged between 6 to 11 years old, showed that children who played video games for, on average, 5 hours per week were more likely to do well in school and get on with their peers [92]. In all such cases, video games elevate alertness by focusing attention and enhancing the brain's processing speed that causes time to subjectively slow down.

It is obvious that we do not all experience the same speed of time. We absorb the world at slightly different processing speeds that depends on several factors that influence our brain's electrical activity levels. Moreover, our ability to sustain attention depends on our short-term memory capacity and that too varies from one person to another. This, in turn, affects the duration of our mental snapshots and how fast our internal clocks tick. These individual differences in brain processing speed and short-term memory capacity are also evident in our personality traits. You could be an introvert or an extrovert, a morning or a night person, someone who easily gets bored or someone who has fun in the dullest moments; an intrinsically motivated person or an extrinsically motivated one, a carefree person or an anxious one, you could be an impulsive person who is always in a hurry, or a more patient one. All these personality traits play an important role in speeding up or slowing down your experience of time because, as we shall see, they are closely related to the brain's alertness level and information processing speed, both crucial factors in time perception. So let us examine these personality traits in order to better understand why we experience time the way we do.

'The type of person you are greatly affects how you experience time'

Introvert or Extrovert?

We previously saw how time slows down when alertness levels are boosted in life-threatening situations, out-of-the-ordinary situations, and times of intense emotion. Alertness levels also vary throughout the day. An hour in the morning feels longer than the same interval in the afternoon because we are more alert in the morning. Moreover, we are all born with a natural level of alertness that varies too from one person to another. We therefore all experience time at varying speeds. This all depends on what neuroscientists call 'cortical arousal' which, in simple terms, means the extent to which our brain is alert and responsive to stimulation. It is a measure of the intrinsic level of brain activity and the speed at which we process sensory information. It is based on our unique temperament, which is partly inherited genetically and, therefore, present from birth. Depending on that innate level of mental arousal, psychologists have recognized two core personality types: extroverts who are more outgoing and talkative, and introverts who enjoy more reserved, reflective, and solitary behavior.

Extroverts thrive when around other people and work well in groups. Most take pleasure in large social gatherings, parties, public demonstrations, and political groups. They prefer active places that are noisy. They are natural multi-taskers, are not easily distracted, dislike repetition and routine, and can easily get bored when alone. Some famous extroverts are Oprah, Barak Obama, Margret Thatcher, Steve Jobs, Winston Churchill, and Queen Marie Antoinette.

On the other hand, introverts take pleasure in solitary activities such as reading, writing, hiking, and fishing where they can get internal stimulation. They enjoy spending time alone and prefer to concentrate on one activity at a time for they can be easily distracted. They are best in situations where they are able to reflect on their own, rather than interacting with others. Introversion is not to be confused with shyness or antisocial behavior. Most artists, writers, sculptors, engineers, composers, inventors are highly introverted. Examples of famous introverts are Bill Gates, Christina Aguilera, Albert Einstein, Emma Watson, David Lettermen, and Moses. Approximately 60 percent of gifted children and 75 percent of highly gifted children are introverted.

So what kind of person are you? An introvert or an extrovert? Most likely a bit of both. Most of us fall somewhere in the middle of the scale, that is to say, we all have both introverted and extroverted aspects in our personalities but tend to lean to one type more than the other. It is rare to come across extreme extroverts or introverts but people with severe mental disorders and psychopathic tendencies are often found to be at the extreme ends of the scale. There are several websites that provide personality tests for determining your level of introversion. Based on that level, we will shortly see that you can figure out how fast time runs in your mind. A good self-test that should not take more than 25 minutes to complete can be found at Psychology Today website [93].

To explain the basis of these personality differences, psychologist Hans Eysenck introduced the theory of arousal in 1967, in an influential book titled *Dimensions of Personality*. Dr. Eysenck found that introverts have chronically higher cortical (mental) arousal levels by nature, and are innately over-stimulated which causes them to be easily overwhelmed by too much stimulation. This explains why they prefer activities that are more solitary. They tend to avoid situations that involve intense stimulation and prefer quiet places with minimal people. This means that if you were to put an introvert in a loud party, they would quickly become overloaded, causing them to mentally shut down. They avoid such active environments in an effort to reduce the influx of information. They may be motivated to pursue simple activities such as reading or watching a movie to maintain balance in their mental arousal levels. Because of their higher arousal levels, they tend to be edgy, tense, oversensitive, easily irritable, and always in a rush.

Extroverts, on the other hand, possess lower mental arousal levels, so they tend to be relaxed, easy-going, calm, and laid-back. They seek more stimulation from the external environment to compensate for their low levels of cortical arousal. They 'feel more alive' in the company of other people. They are sensation seekers that often desire thrill and adventure, such as engaging in dangerous sports and, sometimes, even seeking negative emotions such as fear, which explains why horror movies are so popular. Extroverts are minimally aroused by nature, so they need to work harder to stimulate their minds to the same level that introverts might easily reach. This leads extroverts to seek novelty, adventure, or any highly stimulating environments to supplement their lack of mental arousal.

These differences in personality have been illustrated in countless studies. One such study was conducted at the University of Missouri where researchers asked 70 extroverts and 70 introverts to select the music volume that they preferred while performing a learning task. They found that extroverts consistently chose significantly louder music than introverts, which supports the idea that they seek more sensory stimulation. When the researchers switched the music levels so that the introverts now had the louder music and vice versa, the extroverts became bored and the introverts became upset and needed more time to perform the task. You know you are an extrovert if you are able to work better with music or the TV in the background, or an introvert if you find it too distracting [94].

A large number of studies have shown that the brains of introverts and extroverts are really quite different. In one study, scientists measured the amount of blood that flows into the brains of introverted and extroverted people using positron emission tomography (PET) scans and found that introverts have more blood flow in their frontal lobes, which are brain regions involved in recalling events, making plans, and solving problems. Extroverts, on the other hand, have more blood flow in brain areas involved in detecting sensory information. As expected, this suggests that extroverts tend to focus their attention outwards, while introverts focus their attention inwards. Another indication of the level of extroversion is the amount of saliva you produce when putting a drop of lemon on your tongue. In an interesting 'lemon juice experiment', scientists confirmed that introverts salivate more than extroverts in response to a drop of lemon juice, because of their higher level of mental arousal and more sensitive response to stimuli, the lemon juice in this case.

Scientists have confirmed a direct link between the level of introversion and the subjective speed of time. Studies have shown that, because of their higher mental arousal levels, introverts can detect higher fusion frequencies for flickering lights compared to extroverts. Higher levels of arousal in introverts also mean faster processing of sensory information and faster recording of mental snapshots which, as we saw earlier, implies a fast-ticking internal clock. In contrast, extroverts have intrinsically lower levels of mental arousal and, therefore, their internal clock ticks at a slower rate.

In a 2001 study that investigated the effects of personality on time, researchers tested undergraduate students from the psychology department at the Louisiana State University to see how accurately they could reproduce one minute in their mind. For introverted students, their faster internal clock led them to estimate that one minute has passed in 58 seconds. While for extroverts, 77 seconds had to pass for their slower internal clock to measure one minute of real time [95]. This 17-second difference for every passing minute is quite substantial and can add up over time. In one hour, an extrovert would be 17 minutes late. According to this study, extroverts' internal clocks tick up to 30% slower than introverts. It is, therefore, important to understand where your personality lies on the spectrum of extroversion-introversion so that you can appreciate how fast or how slow time runs in your mind compared to the real flow of time. You can then make adjustments in your daily life to compensate for that speed difference. Let us look at a few practical examples.

If an introvert and an extrovert both watch a one-hour movie without being aware of the passing time and with no prior knowledge of the movie duration, and you ask them how long they thought it ran for after it has finished, the introvert's faster internal clock will cover a longer duration of around one hour and 18 minutes. He will over-estimate its duration and will feel that the movie dragged. Whereas, the extrovert's slower internal clock will cover a shorter duration of say 43 minutes only (during that actual one hour movie), so he will underestimate its duration and feel that time flew. The same duration perceived *retrospectively* will subjectively expand in an introvert's mind and shrink in that of an extrovert. Introverts' brains will count more time within a fixed time duration when compared to extroverts' brains who will count less time. This difference in time estimation is one of the reasons why extroverts are generally happier than introverts. We saw in the previous chapter how time flies when you are having fun and drags when you are bored. We also saw that people tend to judge activities as more pleasant if they felt that time flew, and unpleasant if they felt that time dragged. Since time tends to fly for extroverts, they will *retrospectively* perceive their activities to be more fun in comparison with introverts who perceive time as have been dragging, and thus was boring. The extrovert will tend to enjoy the movie more than the introvert. This effect applies to activities where someone (an introvert or extrovert) is not intentionally keeping track of time and only judge how long an activity has been going *after* the fact. This is the type of *retrospective* time estimation that we saw in Chapter 1. This differs from *prospective* time estimation, when someone is intentionally keeping track of the passing time. As we shall see next, this effect on retrospective time estimation produces contradictory results in activities that involve a prospective experience of time. These activities rely on guessing when a certain time duration will be over when fully aware of the passing time. Let us look at an example.

Imagine an introvert and an extrovert each cooking a roasted chicken that requires one hour in an oven. This does not involve estimating time that has already elapsed, like in the movie example (retrospective time estimation), but involves guessing when one hour will elapse in order to switch off the oven (prospective time estimation). The main difference between the two is that while watching the movie, they were both unaware of the passing time while in the cooking example, they are fully conscious of its passing. The introvert's faster internal clock will reach one hour earlier than a real clock and he will guess that one hour has passed in less than an hour. He will switch off the oven too early and chicken is undercooked. The extrovert, on the other hand, will guess that the one-hour cooking time is over in more than one hour, because of his slower internal clock, and will switch off the oven too late resulting in an overcooked chicken.

The prospective time experience implies that when introverts are involved in activities where they are aware of the passing time, they will view time as limited and valuable. This explains why they tend to always be in a hurry. According to the Louisiana study, one hour will prospectively feel 15 minutes short when introverts are planning the duration of things they want to do and so their day ahead will feel shorter. This means that they tend to be more conscious of how they manage their precious time. For extroverts, on the other hand, their slower internal clock will, according to that study, need one hour and 17 minutes of real time for them to guess that one subjective hour has passed. When they are aware of the passing time, an hour will feel like it contains 17 more minutes. That is why extroverts are more laid-back and see the time ahead as more abundant (prospectively). They take their time in almost everything they do and are rarely in a rush. An extrovert's slower internal clock also explains why they tend to miss appointments! Therefore, if you are constantly late and cannot figure out why, you are most likely an extrovert and it would be wise to give yourself 20 to 30% more time to meet a deadline or to get to an appointment.

You will note from the two examples that the resulting time experience is contradictory depending on whether the time judgment is done prospectively or retrospectively. It might sound a bit confusing, so let us quickly recap. When introverts, with their faster internal clocks, look back at an activity they did without being aware of the passing time and try to *retrospectively* estimate how long it took, it will stretch in their mind, as if time dragged. In contrast, when they are aware of the passing time and trying to *prospectively* guess when a certain activity will be over, they will under-estimate it, as if time is running quickly.

The opposite applies to extroverts. With their slower internal clocks, when they look back at an activity they did and try to *retrospectively* estimate how long it took, it will shrink in their mind, as if time flew. In contrast, when extroverts are aware of the passing time and trying to *prospectively* guess when a certain duration will elapse, they will over-estimate it, as if time is running slowly. You will experience these time distortions depending on where your personality lies on the spectrum of introversion.

'Extroverts' internal clocks tick up to 30% slower than introverts'

How Quickly Do You Get Bored?

Another personality trait that affects our perceived speed of time is how easily we get bored. We have all experienced a lazy, boring Sunday morning that crawls compared to a busy Monday morning that passes in a flash. Ask any elderly person living in a care home how he feels about time. He will tell you it is passing very slowly due to the monotonous days [96]. Boredom is a transient unpleasant emotional state experienced when you are left without anything in particular to do or when you lose interest in your surroundings. Existential philosophers, like Jean-Paul Sartre and Albert Camus, claim that boredom is just a human response to the meaninglessness of life. They assert that no matter how much enjoyment you get from something, sooner or later you will get bored with it and start looking for something new. No matter how many new experiences you engage in or how many interesting things you are able to buy, you will eventually get bored with them. This urge to keep busy with novelty and to escape the present is our greatest source of unhappiness, argues the distinguished Danish philosopher, Kierkegaard. According to these great thinkers, boredom is essentially a part of life, an inescapable aspect of the human condition.

Today's teenagers, in particular, are more vulnerable to boredom due to a combination of overstimulation from TV, computers, tablets, mobile phones, etc., and a lack of coping skills when the action dies down. If you asked teenagers in the 19th century what they did in their free time, they would probably talk about helping their parents at work. If you ask the same question to teenagers in the mid 1990's, you might get an answer related to baseball, football, or the latest playground craze. But nowadays, most teens would reply video games or social media. Studies reveal that American teenagers spend an average of 6.5 hours a day focused on electronic devices. This invasion of electronic products into children's lives causes over-simulation in terms of their attention. They are constantly looking for more stimulation and when that is not found, they easily get bored. For many teenagers, being bored seems to be the new cool. This is reflected in clothing that suggests a bored blasé attitude to life is far cooler than the usual enthusiasm that characterizes young children. This effort to curb enthusiasm is also seen in many adults. We seem to be living in an age where it is trendy to look perpetually bored, dissatisfied, and uninterested! But is there a scientific basis for this boredom syndrome? And how does it affect our perception of time?

One aspect of Dr. Eysenck's arousal theory is that we all seem to have a basic boredom threshold that is unique to us. It is defined as the amount of stimulation we must receive before we feel aroused, and it determines our innate vulnerability to boredom. Below that level, we are less happy and, above it, we are happier and having fun. Introverts generally have a low boredom threshold, so they need little stimulation to keep them happy. They get bored less often and manage to find something interesting in the even dull situations. Extroverts, on the other hand, have a higher threshold and require greater stimulation before they become mentally aroused, so they tend to be impatient and can easily get bored when that stimulation is lacking. Extroverts also tend to have a shorter span of attention so they are unable to focus on an activity for very long. Therefore, they easily get distracted by external events. As a result, they are unable to maintain the necessary motivation to complete that activity and become more aware of the passing of time. As we saw previously, this *prospective* experience of the time-in-passing causes time to run slowly.

The boredom threshold depends on our brain's overall level of alertness and cortical arousal. That is why boredom is closely related to the level of introversion. By measuring brain electrical activity with EEG, neuroscientists find that high-sensation seekers have lower overall alertness than low-sensation seekers. This explains why they are in constant need for stimulation. Knowing where your personality stands on the extroversion-introversion spectrum will determine how easily you get bored.

In the United States, statistics indicate that people are split 50/50 between introverts and extroverts. However, society in general is biased towards extroverts. The education system, by its nature, favors extroverts because it requires children to learn in big classrooms, which will naturally provide a high-stimulation environment. Group activities, 'show and tell', and speaking in class all favor the extrovert. Introverted and reclusive children would prefer one-on-one schooling, away from group learning. But that is not economically viable and so schools end up turning into a place where introverted kids learn to *act* like extroverts. Similarly, businesses that involve sales and marketing favor the outgoing extrovert, which is why many introverts tend to feign extroversion to get ahead. This might explain why looking bored and disinterested seems fashionable these days.

Men are, generally, more likely to get bored than women and this is why they enjoy more dangerous entertainment, and are more inclined towards high-risk lifestyles. People who are most prone to boredom have a greater tendency to end up with some form of addiction. They tend to be impulsive, restless, and impatient with routine. They seek exciting activities like mountain climbing and bungee jumping. If you know what a person does for fun, you can easily tell how prone to boredom he or she is and to what extent he or she is introverted or extroverted.

Our perceived speed of time depends on how easily we get bored. Imagine a quiet day spent relaxing at home, reading or watching TV. If you are an introvert, this might be comfortable. It is just at the limit of your boredom threshold and the day passes swiftly. But, for an extrovert, this would be unbearable. He would be restless and the day would drag. A slightly more interesting day would be at the office. An introvert has the chance of some social interaction but can withdraw to his office when he needs some quiet time. The extrovert is only slightly better off here and would probably still be restless. Time would still drag but not as much as the day at home. Now move into a crowded pub and the extrovert might find just enough stimulation to feel right. Time is now moving at a speed that is fast enough to make the experience entertaining. But for the introvert, this is slightly above their boredom threshold and the night will feel stretched. Even worse would be a loud night club. It goes well beyond the introvert's comfort zone. But, for the extrovert, they are in their element, charging up their batteries, and deriving immense pleasure from that level of stimulation. This provides them with so much fun that time flies and the night is over in a blink.

Regardless of your boredom threshold, the good news is that boredom is among the emotions that we usually do not experience for very long. That said, there are still some ways that we can make time seem like it is going faster on a dull day. Some people try to kill boredom by finding thrilling or exciting experiences. These could range from seeking novelty, such as rollercoaster rides or learning to ski, to rule-breaking and drug use. Such activities provide the brain with a surge of dopamine that produces ecstatic sensations. However, this is only temporary and quickly becomes ineffective. No matter how novel the activity is, when it is done regularly, it will become familiar and eventually boring. When the action fades away, the dopamine levels quickly drop back to normal, producing a greater feeling of emptiness than before. An example could be base jumpers who strive for harder and more dangerous jumps each time to keep up their dopamine levels.

Another trick we all use to kill boredom is distraction. When standing in a queue or sitting in a waiting room, most of us reach out for our smartphone to check our Facebook, Twitter, or Instagram accounts; anything that will distract us from the passage of time and cause it to run faster. When bored at home, distractions could be watching TV, playing computer games, or preparing a tasty snack, (which we might later feel guilty about)! At work, we may look outside the window, take breaks, chat with some colleagues, surf the internet, or daydream; anything that diverts our attention from the slow passage of time. But these quick solutions are only temporary. Time distractions might seem great when we have free time to kill, but if they become addictive, such as eating junk food or being permanently attached to social media, the effects could be damaging. The end result is often a bad feeling that time has been wasted since it was not used to pursue meaningful goals.

The best strategy for dealing with boredom is to make use of the time in a meaningful way. When you feel that time has been spent efficiently, you will feel it is running faster. The best way to achieve that is to perform the boring task in the mental state of 'flow' that we saw in Chapter 5. That involves focusing on the task itself rather than on the time it is taking. This requires understanding the challenges and mustering the motivation to meet those challenges and be rewarded for that achievement. As a result, you become fully immersed 'in the zone' to the extent that you lose track of time and kill any thoughts of boredom.

Another aspect to consider when you are doing something boring is your motivation for doing it. Are you intrinsically motivated, that is, do you derive pleasure, enjoyment, and satisfaction from that activity? Or are you motivated by external incentives that are distinct from the activity itself? These might include financial reward, or helping out a friend or colleague. Intrinsic motivation is when, for instance, you read books simply because you enjoy reading, whereas extrinsic motivation is when you read for the purpose of passing your college exam. When you are intrinsically motivated to do something you will be more creative and able to maintain your interest for longer periods. But when you are extrinsically motivated, your focus is not on the work itself since it does not provide you with direct satisfaction. You consider your work only as a means to an end and you will be checking the time more often so you can get it over as quickly as possible. Your awareness of the passing time makes it appear unpleasant and it will therefore drag. Extrinsic motivation enhances feelings of boredom. In contrast, if you are intrinsically motivated, your focus is mainly on your work and whatever personal rewards and satisfaction it may bring. As a result, you will be less concerned about the time it takes and it will be a more enjoyable experience.

One last thing to keep in mind is that, sometimes, boredom can be a beneficial feeling. Without boredom, there would be no daydreaming and no room for reflection. Without reflection and contemplation, there is no imagination and creativity, and without creativity, no inventions, art, or progress. Boredom is just the dark side of fun for they both share the same brain circuitry. Life would not be fun at all without a little boredom!

Night Owl or Morning Lark?

If you work in a large company, you may have noticed how at the beginning of the day, sleepy people queue up at the coffee counter to get their morning fix of caffeine. These people describe themselves as not 'morning people' and it is hard to engage them in any meaningful conversation before they have consumed at least one cup of coffee. Towards the end of the working day, you will notice another queue building up at the coffee counter, but this time it is a different crowd. These are the 'morning people' who wake up early for a workout at the gym or a quick run. By mid-afternoon, their energy levels have dropped and so they are in need of a quick boost of caffeine.

Everyone has a noticeably different rhythm of sleeping and waking-known as *circadian rhythm*- which is why psychologists divide people into two general chronotypes: morning larks and night owls. Morning larks rise early, are most active in the morning, grow tired more quickly by late afternoon or early evening and go to bed early. By contrast, night owls need a few hours to fully awake in the morning, become active in the evenings, and sleep late. They tend to be novelty seekers and have personalities that are consistent with outgoing extroverts. Most children start out as morning larks. If you have children, you know how it feels when they wake you up in the early morning. When they turn into teenagers, they become night owls, going to late-night parties, and this continues until their early twenties, when they turn back to morning larks once again, or sometimes stay as night owls.

Personality chronotypes depend on how alertness and concentration levels vary during the day, or what is known as the *concentration curve*. Concentration is defined as the amount of time you can focus on a single thought or mental activity. Concentration levels vary depending on who you are with, what you are doing, how interesting it is, and whether you had a nice bottle of wine for lunch. But, more importantly, concentration and alertness depend on the time of day. For morning larks, alertness and concentration levels start high and decline as the day progresses, while for night owls, this happens in reverse: alertness and concentration levels start low and rise steadily with the passing hours. So, how does our personality chronotype affect our perception of time?

Alertness levels vary during the day for each chronotype, and since the perceived speed of time depends on alertness and arousal levels, then it follows that the speed of time changes for each chronotype as the day goes by. Scientists have confirmed that the internal clock of morning-type people generally runs faster than that of evening-types [97]. For the morning-type person, alertness levels are normally at their highest in the morning and then start to drop towards the afternoon after a decent lunch, until it reaches its lowest levels in the evening. As the alertness levels drop, the brain's information processing speed decreases and the internal clock slows down, so time intervals shrink, and time appears to pass quickly. For the morning person, the afternoon is often over in a flash. With the feeling of abundant time early in the day, morning larks tend to be more productive and can achieve more in the morning than in the afternoon. Therefore, an hour in the morning will generally feel longer than an hour in the afternoon.

The opposite happens for a night-type person. Alertness levels are low in the morning and start to increase towards the afternoon, reaching their highest level in the evening. This means that the brain's information processing and internal clock start to speed up as the day goes by, so time intervals stretch and time gradually slows down as the day passes. For night owls, mornings fly by and afternoons drag, which makes them more productive in the second half of the day.

Alertness and concentration levels in each chronotype affect performance and a number of studies have confirmed this. A study on professional Olympic swimmers, who tend to be night owls, found that they were 2.7 seconds faster when swimming for 100 meters at 10:00 p.m., than swimming the same distance at 6 a.m. Another study looked at 16 Major League Baseball players- nine owls and seven larks- and compared their game statistics from nearly 7,500 innings during the 2009-2010 seasons. The results indicated that when morning larks played early games (before 2 p.m.) or when night owls played night games, they both hit higher scores than when game times conflicted with their chronotypes. The performance of night owls suffered the most when they played in day games [98].

With that in mind and, since it is not easy to change your chronotype, it would be advisable to organize your life around your concentration curve for optimal performance. This means playing to your strengths and using your prime time for the activities that require higher levels of concentration, while shifting the less demanding activities to that time of the day when your concentration levels are low. Match your work routine to your chronotype to optimize productivity and slow down time when you needed it most.

Of course, this is easier said than done. Especially for people who get up late, since society is generally calibrated for the early risers. Schools, businesses, and hospitals normally start between 8 and 9 o'clock, and sometimes even earlier. Therefore, late risers often experience a mismatch between their chronotype and society. Their sleeping pattern makes it difficult for them to sleep early and the alarm clock wakes them up too soon. As a result, they accumulate a sleep deficit over the course of a week, which is only partially recovered on the weekend. This explains why night owls tend to drink more coffee to stay awake during the day, and more alcohol to help them fall asleep at night. To improve performance and reduce sleep deficit, more companies are now introducing flextime, allowing employees to alter the start and finish of a working day. Because teenagers tend to be night owls with different sleeping patterns than children, in 1997 seven high schools in the Minneapolis Public School District shifted the school start time from 7:15 a.m. to 8:40 a.m. A long-term study was then carried out that involved assessing 18,000 high school students to see how it affected their school performance [99]. The results indicated that students were less sleepy, more alert, less depressive, and had better grades than those students whose school schedule was not adjusted. This is, incidentally, the reason why modern high schools in the U.S. who still start at 8:00 a.m. do not start core subjects before ten o'clock in the morning.

Matching your chronotype to your lifestyle has clear benefits but, when mismatches occur, you can use that to your advantage. In fact, mismatches can sometimes be beneficial, especially when it comes to inducing creativity. In one study, 428 participants had to solve analytical problems, some of which required logical thinking and some of which required moments of creative thought, in morning or late afternoon sessions. What the researchers found was that participants, surprisingly, scored highly on creative problems when they did the tests at their non-optimal time of the day. It seems that creative ideas flourish when people are mentally tired, in a similar way to how taking a break from a problem can produce unexpected insights [100]. This leads us to another important personality trait that affects the speed of time.

'Match your work routine to your chronotype to optimize productivity'

Impulsive or Self-Controlled?

Are you generally impulsive or self-controlled? Patient or impatient? This personality trait is also a direct product of the speed of your internal clock. Impulsive people tend to perceive time as moving slowly compared to patient and more restrained people [101]. This is important and affects a lot of the decisions you make, especially those where you have to choose between an immediate or delayed reward. For instance, if you were considering whether to go on a diet and lose weight, you would be assessing the health benefits and improved appearance that you would gain, against the temporary loss of pleasure in eating certain foods. If it was going to take you one month to reach your targeted weight, you would consider the 'loss' of all those tasty foods that you would have eaten in that month. If you were an impulsive person, your slower internal clock would cause the forthcoming month to appear longer than it really is. So the 'loss' in food pleasures would be amplified in your mind, meaning that giving up on the diet would be more likely.

That is why extroverts and night owls tend to be overweight. The popular image of fat people being fun and jolly is actually based on scientific fact. A study of around 30,000 Japanese people aged between 40 and 64 found that extroverts were mostly overweight whereas introversion was closely associated with being underweight. The study concluded that being impulsive is the strongest indicator of obesity, and extroverts tend to be more impulsive, sensation seekers, and risk-takers that easily get bored, in comparison to introverts [102]. Any future time interval that is imagined in the mind of an extrovert or night owl will *prospectively* feel longer, due to their slower internal clock. This causes their patience to run out faster than introverts or morning larks and so will easily give up any planned diet.

One way to determine if you have an impulsive personality would be to ask yourself a hypothetical question such as: 'Would you prefer $1,000 right now or $2,000 in a week?' These types of decisions are influenced by how fast you perceive time as running. Impulsive people tend to put less value on delayed rewards in comparison to patient people, who postpone impulsive urges of immediate gratification in return for a much higher future reward later on. Impulsive people will prefer smaller and immediate rewards to larger and delayed rewards because they estimate time durations as being subjectively longer. If your time perception causes you to feel that a future reward is further away than it is really is, you will assess the cost as too high and you will prefer a more immediate outcome.

If you are a student, for instance, who is trying to decide whether to go to a party tonight or stay at home and study for tomorrow's exam, the immediate reward is the fun you derive from the party, but the delayed reward is, of course, passing the exam. Impulsive students will go for the immediate reward because time spent studying, and not attending the party, will pass by excruciatingly slowly. Anything that extends the perceived duration of an imagined future time interval will make you more impulsive. It could be a sad emotional state that decreases your mental arousal level and the speed of your internal clock. Or it could be a built-in feature of your personality. The greater the expansion of time durations in your mind, the more anxious you will be that the future reward is far from being attained. In such cases, you will be motivated to choose the immediate satisfaction over the delayed reward. This brings us to the last personality trait that influences our speed of time: trait anxiety.

Trait Anxiety: How Often do you Worry?

We saw in the previous chapter on emotions how anxiety slows time. This is the effect of short-term 'state anxiety' which nearly everyone experiences from time to time. An example is being nervous about an upcoming school exam, or your medical test results or your financial situation. However, anxiety can also be long-term; a consistent personality trait. People, for instance, who are constantly worried about their health, to the point of paranoia, have trait anxiety in their character. People with a high level of built-in 'trait anxiety' have a greater tendency to be nervous at the slightest cause for worry. Their anxiety also tends to be much more intense, sometimes accompanied by panic attacks, and concerns a broader range of everyday situations. Most people, for instance, might be naturally nervous when they are meeting a very important or famous person. But people with trait anxiety would be anxious before meeting anyone new. Another example is being nervous when traveling to a new place or moving into a new city. That would be 'state anxiety' to some degree. But someone with trait anxiety would faint at the idea of moving to any new place. This intense nervousness produced by the built-in trait anxiety is what causes time to slow down even more for people with this personality type.

We all have some level of 'trait' anxiety in our personalities, even those of us who boast having nerves of steel. It is important to understand how much trait anxiety is in your personality, to understand how it influences your experience of the speed of time, and to find ways to counteract that. A simple psychological test called '*State-Trait Anxiety Inventory*' is the standard for measuring trait anxiety. A few websites offer simple free versions of this test which can be used to give you an idea of where you are on the scale [103]. Treatments for trait anxiety range from simple psychological treatments, such as graded exposure and fostering an optimistic and positive attitude, to medical attention for the more severe anxiety disorders. Without going into further detail, it suffice to say that trait anxiety will slow time in your mind even more than the occasional state anxiety, so it is advisable to take a quick test and find out how much time distortion this is causing you.

Recap

To sum up, several aspects of your personality affect the speed at which you perceive time. Your brain's internal clock will run faster if you are an introvert or a morning lark, a patient and self-controlled person or someone who worries a lot, someone who does not easily get bored or a combination of all those traits. As a consequence, when you look back at the time you have spent doing something (retrospective time experience), it will often seem to have dragged. That is because your brain has covered more time internally then the rest of the outside world did. As for prospective experience of time, your faster internal clock will make you feel that you have less time for activities you are planning to complete in the future. You will therefore perceive time as more scarce and feel a constant rush.

In contrast, your brain's internal clock will run more slowly if you are an extrovert, or a night owl, an impulsive person, or a boredom-prone person, or any combination of the those traits. When you look back at the time you spent doing something, it will retrospectively seem to have flown by. This is because your brain covered less time internally then the rest of the world did. The duration of activities you were engaged in will tend to shrink in your mind. On the other hand, when planning ahead, your slower internal clock will need more time to produce durations for activities you are planning in your mind. Future duration will stretch and you will not feel hurried since you will feel that time is abundant and you can complete tasks in less time than is actually needed.

That said, knowing how your personality traits affect your experience of time can be used to your advantage. Certain traits are genetically inherited and cannot be changed, but you can work around those to suit your ultimate goals. You can try, for example, to organize your work around your chronotype and concentration curve. If you easily get bored, distraction will only waste your time. Instead, you can learn to spend time in a more meaningful way by converting boring activities into flow-inducing ones, as seen in chapter 5. When you have no choice but to go through routine, you can slow things down by finding value and intrinsic motivation in doing things for their own sake. If you tend to worry a lot, you can try to get into the habit of thinking positively to shorten the duration of those anxious moments.

Another factor that effects time perception, and which we will explore next, is the effect of certain mind-altering drugs and medications. By directly tinkering with the brain's chemicals processes, time can be made to slow down, speed up, or even freeze to a complete halt! In the next chapter, we will explore that, keeping in mind that, in no way, do I endorse the use of any harmful drugs for that purpose.

CHAPTER 9

MESSING WITH TIME

THE EFFECT OF DRUGS AND MENTAL DISORDERS

'O time, suspend your flight!'
— Lamartine, 1820

Intellectual Rave Club

On a cold December night in 1846, in a remote quarter in the middle of Paris, a number of leading Parisian intellectuals gather in a strange club that has recently been formed. Great writers and artists including Alexandre Dumas, Victor Hugo, Honoré de Balzac, Charles Baudelaire, Eugène Delacroix and many others enter an old house on Ile St Louis for their monthly meeting at the newly founded *Club des Hashischins* (Club of the Hasheesh Eaters). The purpose of the meeting is to explore the mind-altering effects of the recently discovered marijuana herb. Fifty years earlier, Napoleon had invaded Egypt on his way to India and his troops had discovered the cannabis plant, which they brought back to France after being expelled in 1801. The plant was an instant hit, especially with the aristocrats and nobility. The club ran for about 5 years and the intellectuals reported a mixture of experiences like euphoria, hallucination, and extremely rapid flow of ideas. Charles Baudelaire, author of *Les Fleurs du Mal* and one of the founding members of the club, wrote '...a new stream of ideas carries you away. It will hurl you along in its living vortex for a further minute; and this minute, too, will be an eternity, for the normal relation between time and the individual is completely upset by the multitude and intensity of sensations and ideas. You seem to live several men's lives in the space of an hour.' He also notes, '...your senses become extraordinarily keen and acute. Your sight is infinite. Your ear can discern the slightest perceptible sound. The slightest ambiguities, the most inexplicable transpositions of ideas take place. In sounds there is color; in colors there is a music. This fantasy goes on for an eternity. A lucid interval and a great expenditure of effort, permit you to look at the clock. The eternity turns out to have been only a minute.' The club broke up later in 1849, but not after it had done its work with the publication of the first scientific book on cannabis by Dr. Morceau. The book *De Hachish et de l'Alienation Mentale* contained interesting recounts about the time-distorting experiences resulting from cannabis consumption. The French doctor, Charles Richet, summed it up nicely, "with hashish the notion of time is completely overthrown. The moments are years, and the minutes are centuries."

People from various cultures report similar experiences with numerous drugs and their influence on the perceived speed of time. In 1955, psychiatrist Dr. Humphry Osmond, who coined the term 'psychedelic', conducted a famous experiment, in which he administered 400 mg of mescaline to British Member of Parliament, Christopher Mayhew, and recorded his experience on camera. In the BBC documentary, *The Beyond Within*, Mayhew described how 'half a dozen times during the experiment, he had a period of time that did not end for him' and that the experiment 'took place outside [of] time.' In his famous book *Confessions of an English Opium Eater*, Thomas De Quincey similarly noted that opium intoxication resulted in distortions to the flow of time to the extent that he 'sometimes seemed to have lived for 70 or 100 years in one night; no, sometimes had feelings representative of a millennium passed in that time!'

It is well established that psychedelic drugs interact with certain brain neurotransmitters and affect the level of electrical activity in the brain. Marijuana, for instance, acts as a dopamine stimulant that boosts the neurons' firing rate and speeds up brainwave frequencies [104]. This, in turn, affects the speed at which the world is perceived and twists the experience of time. Intoxication causes the internal clock to tick faster so that durations expand and time appears to pass slowly [105, 106]. One study found that an audio clip that is 10 seconds long appears to last 12 seconds when under the mild influence of marijuana [107]. The music industry is notably associated with the use of marijuana, or 'weed', due to its time-distorting properties that augment musical performances and appreciation. To a music performer or listener, the time-expanding effect makes music more pleasant and enjoyable. Every musical note appears more intense and seems to last longer. The effect on someone who never smoked marijuana is a sudden heightened sense of alertness and slowing of time, all of which are indicative of a boost in information processing speed [108]. However, this time-expanding effect actually reverses in frequent smokers of marijuana. With long-term usage, the opposite effects are observed and time appears to speed up.

To demonstrate the effect of drug stimulants on time perception, neuroscientist, Warren Meck, carried out an interesting experiment, at Duke University in Durham, on rats that were trained to press a lever to receive a food reward after a period of 12 seconds. To investigate how drugs affect the rats' time perception, he put the rats on cocaine, which is a dopamine stimulant, and found that they started pressing the lever too soon. Cocaine made their internal clock tick faster so that they felt the 12 seconds were already over when only 8 seconds had actually passed. The drugged rats thought that more time had elapsed than actually had, and that those 8 seconds had somehow expanded. In contrast, when he put another group of rats on haloperidol, which is a dopamine blocker, they started pressing the lever too late, indicating that they thought less time had elapsed than actually had. The drug slowed their internal clock to the extent that it took 16 seconds for them to feel that 12 seconds had elapsed [109]. Drugs that stimulate dopamine receptors slow down time and stretches durations, while depressants that inhibit those receptors, speed it up.

Slowing Down Time with Stimulants

As we saw earlier, neuroscientists use Flicker Fusion Frequency (FFF) tests to measure the brain's information processing speed and its state of alertness. When people consume stimulants, like nicotine and amphetamine, their FFF increases [110]. Amphetamines were originally developed as anti-depressants but are now being used as 'mental enhancers' that go by the street names 'speed', 'ice', 'whizz', 'uppers', or 'ecstasy' depending on their composition. Amphetamines raise the level of brain neurotransmitters and enhance alertness by exciting the firing rate of brain neurons which allows the brain to register more events in a shorter period of time, hence the street name 'speed'. This boost to the brain's processing speed increases energy levels, concentration, motivation, and slows down time. During World War II, U.S soldiers were given amphetamine drugs to increase their alertness on the front lines. American bomber pilots used amphetamine pills to stay awake during long missions. It is also thought that British troops consumed around 72 million amphetamine tablets during those times, so much so that this drug was said to have won the Battle of Britain!

As you would expect, the alertness-boosting effect of such smart drugs is why people often report a slowing down of time [54]. This is mainly due to the heightened sense of awareness and focused attention that is quite evident in people on drugs. People who are high on marijuana, amphetamines, or other stimulants seem to be fixated on sensations, thoughts, or imaginings and are often unaware of what is going on around them. They seem to be super-focused on the present as if seeing things for the first time. Colors seem brighter and food tastes better. The drugs seem to hijack the brain's limited amount of attentional resources and focus them on a particular thing, filtering out the surrounding noise and distractions in the process. As a result, whatever comes into focus becomes more intense and that includes the present moment that expands in their mind creating the feeling that time had slowed.

However, the extended usage of 'speed' or steroids can also result in hallucinations, paranoia and a loss of contact with reality. This is because it boosts the amount of dopamine inside the brain to levels that are close to those seen in Schizophrenia. It can also lead to a lack of judgment and a willingness to take reckless risks. This explains why people on these drugs have higher tendencies for compulsive gambling. This is similar to the characteristic gambling and risk-taking tendency that is now being observed in Parkinson's disease patients who take dopamine-enhancing drugs, like L-Dopa, Neupro, or Requip. It is important here to note that all amphetamines are prescription-only drugs and consuming them without a prescription is considered a legal offense.

Similarly, people who take Lysergic Acid Diethylamide (LSD) report a profound increase in brain processing speed and sensory intake, and experience time as slowing down. Gamers who take LSD during online games report how these drugs increase their speed of thought, allowing them to analyze the various distinct options simultaneously before actually performing them, annihilating their opponents, while watching the clock tick in slow motion and having the time to chat with onlookers! Aldous Huxley, author of the book *The Doors of Perception*, believed that LSD was a kind of 'mind-expander' that enhances the senses to the extent that seeing, hearing, and tasting create a much deeper perception of reality. He believed that the brain acted as a "reducing valve" that constrained conscious awareness, while psychedelic drugs act to inhibit this filtering mechanism and open the mind's doors of perception. Imagine a sensory knob with a dial similar to an amplifier that goes from 1 to 10 that defines the rate at which our brains process information from the world around us. When we are normally awake, the dial would be at, say, around four. However, on LSD, the rate of information flow would seem to go up to eight, as more of reality flows to the brain via the senses, and the world appears to run in slow motion as more mental snapshots are processed per second.

LSD has a structure that is very similar to the neurotransmitter, serotonin, which is another key chemical messenger that is heavily involved in visual and emotional processing. LSD actually activates serotonin receptors better than serotonin itself! This turns off brain areas responsible for constraining consciousness, allowing thoughts to flow freely and imagination to go into overdrive. That is why people on LSD experience hallucinations [111]. It is like turning up the volume on a piece of quiet music. The audible parts become more audible and things you could not hear previously become clearer. People on LSD start seeing things as if for the first time. When listening to their favorite song, they hear sounds they never knew were there and often report that time has prospectively slowed down to the extent it froze.

These time-stretching effects are also experienced, but to a lesser effect, with anti-depressant medications, such as Zoloft, Prozac, Celexa, Lexapro, and Paxil. The use of these prescription antidepressants has gone up an alarming 400 percent in the past few decades. Currently, one in ten Americans are taking one of these medications to treat depression. If you are taking any of these medications, you now know that your internal clock will be ticking faster than usual, so that prospective future intervals of time will stretch in your mind and retrospective past durations will shrink.

In contrast to stimulants, depressants such as alcohol, heroin, Xanax, and Valium, decrease alertness and slow down the brain's processing speed, causing time to speed up [112, 113]. A few glasses of wine over dinner will shrink time intervals and make time pass fairly quickly. Alcohol slows down speech, thoughts, and movement, which is why drunken people stumble, fall over chairs, and do other clumsy things. Consuming alcohol also causes a decline in FFF values on the long run. However the impact is not so great for someone who does not consume alcohol frequently, but enough to impair the ability to drive a car, for example [114]. Likewise, people taking sleeping agents, beta-blockers, or antihistamines feel drowsy, sleepy, and have lower flickering fusion limit [115]. In fact, pharmaceutical companies use FFF measurements to assess the impact of new drugs like analgesics, sleeping agents, and psychoactive drugs, on the brain and nervous system. If you regularly take any of these medications, you might feel that time is speeding up. These drugs block the action of neurotransmitters and reduce the neurons' firing speed, causing a slower recording of reality and, therefore, the experience that time is running faster.

'Drugs that stimulate dopamine receptors slow down time, while depressants that inhibit those receptors, speed it up'

Smart Drugs and Mind Expanders

Attempts to enhance the human brain through 'magic potions' date back to the ancient Egyptian, Greek, and Roman times. Olympic athletes in ancient Greece were known to turn to herbal medications, hallucinogens, and wine potions to enhance their performance. In Egypt, archeologists have found hashish and opium in ancient tombs. A series of studies have found traces of cocaine and tobacco in hair samples from Egyptian mummies. Roman gladiators, fighting for their survival, also ingested hallucinogens to deal with the traumas of the arena.

Until the 1980s, the most popular chemicals that people used to enhance mental function were caffeine and nicotine. Caffeine is a stimulant that indirectly increases dopamine neurotransmitters, which speed up the firing rate of brain neurons, and produce the popular 'boosting' effect [116, 117]. The effect of one cup of coffee takes about 25 minutes to kick in and then lasts around 30 minutes. Green tea also contains high levels of caffeine with similar effects, but its action can last up to 4 hours. High doses of caffeine consumption increase the brain's FFF and processing speed, which accelerates the brain's internal clock causing time intervals to expand and time to slow down [118]. This probably explains why music sounds better when you are caffeinated than when you are sleepy or tired.

Smoking a cigarette has a similar effect on time perception. That is because nicotine is essentially a dopamine stimulant that increases the brain's alertness levels, speeding up the brain's internal clock causing duration to stretch retrospectively, as if time had slowed down. A study on French women who smoked an average of 8 cigarettes each day confirmed that nicotine improves alertness, which implies a faster internal clock that stretches time durations [119]. Clement Freud jokes about this when he says, "If you resolve to give up smoking, drinking and loving, you don't actually live longer; it just seems longer!"

However, a brand new class of drugs has started to take over nicotine and caffeine's dominance as the stimulants of choice. Nowadays, 'magic potions' go by modern names such as 'smart drugs', 'cognitive enhancers', or 'nootropic drugs'. Public demand for mind enhancers is running at an all-time high. According to the Nutrition Business Journal, the U.S. annual sales of nutritional supplements that promise to improve memory is now at around 37 billion dollars. People have increasingly realized that our mental faculties are the result of biochemical reactions that can be manipulated with pharmaceutical drugs. The growing interest in 'smart drugs' is also fueled by the notion that some medications that were originally developed for patients with mental illnesses may have a positive effect in healthy people as well.

One very popular 'cognitive enhancer' is Modafinil, also known as Provigil. It was originally developed in France to treat narcolepsy, which is a condition that makes people suddenly fall asleep, but was later discovered to be very effective in enhancing alertness in healthy people too (who take it illegally without a prescription). Research ash shown that Modafinil can keep you awake and alert for 90 hours non-stop; without any of the side effects produced by caffeine, such as jitters, nervousness or agitation. That is almost 4 days of no sleep. It is also non-addictive and does not raise the blood pressure or heart-rate. Consuming 200 mg of Modafinil can make you feel very alert, attentive, and highly energetic, like your brain is firing on all cylinders [120]. It enhances sensory perception, improves mood, and makes ordinary tasks more enjoyable [121]. It is also known to boost short-term memory which is at the basis of our attentive abilities and our experience of time [122]. However, the use of Modafinil is illegal without a doctor's prescription, and I do not endorse it's use in any way that is contrary to that.

Other 'smart drugs' that were originally developed to treat Attention Deficit Disorder (ADD), like Ritalin (also known as Concerta) and Adderall, are now also being used illegally by healthy people to enhance concentration. Ritalin is a stimulant drug and seems to work best in young people, especially students who need to sustain attention and enhance their intellectual capacity. It increases levels of brain dopamine which acts to enhance short-term memory, and boosts attention span, alertness, and reaction time. Studies have shown that Ritalin improves time estimation precision in ADHD children which makes it a candidate for controlling time in healthy individuals [123]. People taking Ritalin also report some feelings of euphoria and a sense of well-being. This brain effect can, however, potentially make Ritalin an addictive drug, which is why it is also illegal without a doctor's prescription and should not be taken without that.

So, is there a future in smart drugs and cognitive enhancers for controlling the speed of time? Many scientists are optimistic that one day special smart drugs will become something people take normally every day. The unrelenting advances in neuroscience are opening the way for developing such smart drugs that target specific brain functions such as memory, attention, alertness, and processing speed, all of which are crucial to our time experience. It is inevitable that the ability to control the experienced speed of time using smart drugs will happen sometime in the near future but, until then, the best advice for a drug-free approach is to rely on a good brain diet that will help us maintain a healthy brain, as briefly discussed in Chapter 6. I would just add here that there are several tested and tried natural alternatives to anti-depressant medications, such as garlic, ginger, saffron, turmeric, and curcumin that have similar stimulant properties and can almost do the same job. A diet that is rich with these spices have been shown to stimulate the brain and boost its information processing speed, hence slowing down the perceived speed of time. Of course, it is highly advisable to consult your doctor before taking any dietary supplements.

Time and Mental Disorders

Additional evidence for how brain chemicals affect time perception comes from patients with mental disorders. Patients suffering from Parkinson's disease, Schizophrenia, and Attention Deficit Hyperactivity Disorder (ADHD), all have abnormal levels of neurotransmitters in their brains and experience problems with time perception [124]. These symptoms generally improve when patients receive medications that restore the optimal levels [125].

As we saw already, the neurotransmitter Dopamine is critical to the brain's information processing speed. The more dopamine in your brain, the sharper your attention and alertness are and the faster you can capture and process information through your senses. This implies a faster ticking internal clock and the perception that time is passing slowly. A low level of dopamine makes concentration and focus very difficult and is the culprit in children with Attention Deficit Hyperactivity Disorder (ADHD). Children with ADHD, have difficulty in estimating time intervals due to their limited span of attention and poor concentration. Their brains' pattern of electrical activity shows a reduction in beta brainwaves which are associated with focused attention. The lower dopamine levels and decline in brain electrical activity reduces alertness and causes their brain processing speed to slow down, so less information is recorded. Consequently time appears to speed up in their mind, making them less tolerant to delays and leading to their characteristic impulsive and impatient behavior [126].

Moreover, when alertness levels are low, ADHD children search for external stimulation to keep themselves alert. To understand this, imagine that you are feeling very sleepy in the middle of an important but dull meeting. To keep yourself awake, you might feel the need to talk to the person next to you, maybe stand up and walk around, or take a drink of water. ADHD children feel the same way when they are compelled to sit still and focus on something that is of no interest to them. They start to generate high intensity movements, such as fiddling, doodling, or fidgeting with their hands or feet. They use these body movements to self-regulate alertness and maintain an optimal level of interest. Their impulsive hyperactive behavior and inattentiveness is simply a reaction to the lack of stimulation. This is why doctors prescribe stimulant drugs, like Ritalin and Adderall, which raise dopamine levels and increase brain electrical activity, alertness, and concentration power, so that they no longer need to act impulsively. The stimulants fill the gap in the stimulation they are lacking and seeking.

The same goes for Parkinson's disease, which occurs when the nerve cells that produce dopamine die off. As a result, the brains of Parkinson's disease patients contain almost no dopamine, their alertness and brain processing speed is very low, so that their internal clock ticks very slowly and durations shrink retrospectively resulting in the experience that time ran fast [124]. Since dopamine also plays an important role in controlling body motion, this leads to the characteristic jerky movement and the tendency to "freeze". Moreover, patients with ADHD and Parkinson's disorders cannot detect fast flickering lights and have lower average values of FFF than healthy individuals, which implies a slower 'recording' speed and, hence, a faster flow of subjective time [127].

To remedy this condition, neuroscientists came up with a medication (L-Dopa) which chemically mimics dopamine and restores it to its normal level. This was described by neurologist, Oliver Sacks, in his 1973 cult book *Awakenings* which was later made into a 1990 film by the same name, starring Robin Williams and Robert De Niro. The book tells the story of a group of patients suffering from a sleeping sickness (similar to Parkinson's) that caused their internal clocks to tick so slowly that they seem to have stopped. These patients froze as if in a statue-like condition, speechless, and motionless in their wheelchairs for many decades, until Sacks began treating them with L-Dopa. This restored their dopamine levels, which greased their brain's rusty engine and started their internal clock ticking again. They then started moving again, demonstrating that they had been conscious all along but 'frozen' in their consciousness.

On the other hand, when dopamine levels are higher than normal, people become over-stimulated, paranoid, and suspicious. It increases their brain processing speed and heightens the sensitivity of all their senses, as if turning up the volume in hearing, vision, smell, touch, and taste. At extreme dopamine levels, people can start hearing voices, see hallucinations, experience delusions, and eventually loose contact with reality leading to Schizophrenia. In contrast to ADHD and Parkinson's disease, Schizophrenic patients perceive time as flowing slowly. Schizophrenia is the result of an overactive dopamine system that is characterized by increased gamma brainwave activity. That is why medication that blocks dopamine receptors, such as Clozaril and Seroquel, tends to suppress the symptoms of schizophrenia. Schizophrenia causes people to stop perceiving time as a continuous flow, but rather as something that stops and starts again, as if there is a delay in time perception. Schizophrenics act in a similar way to people under the influence of LSD. Both have abnormally high levels of dopamine, which speeds up their brain processing speed and causes time to slow down to the extent that it feels as if the flow of time has ground to a halt.

It's all in your Eyes

Knowing how much dopamine your brain is running on will give a fair indication of how fast time runs inside your mind. The levels of dopamine also affects the level of mental arousal which, as we saw in the previous chapter, define personality traits, such as extroversion and impulsiveness, and affect the perceived speed of time. But to measure your level of brain dopamine accurately, you will have to undergo a Positron Emission Tomography (PET), which is a rather expensive and invasive medical procedure that involves injecting radioactive elements into your blood stream. If you are not too excited about doing that, there is fortunately an alternative cheaper way to gauge your dopamine levels, and it's all in your eyes. Scientists have discovered that the faster your eyes blink, the higher the levels of your brain dopamine. The average eye blink rate for a healthy brain is between 13 to 17 blinks per minute and is independent of age, eye color, or whether one is wearing eyeglasses [128]. The eye blink rate (EBR) is an easy way to assess mental disorders that are due to abnormal levels of dopamine. Parkinson's disease patients with low dopamine levels blink their eyes less than normal- an average of 11 blinks per minute- whereas schizophrenics blink around 31 blinks per minute [129]. The eye blink rate of long-term chronic marijuana users is lower than normal, indicating lower dopamine levels and slower brainwaves (but it is higher for infrequent users) [130]. By counting how many times someone's eyes blink per minute, you can tell a lot about what is going inside their brain, determine some innate personality traits, mental arousal levels, and how fast time is running in their mind. All other things being equal, people who blink less than the normal range have a slower internal clock. They exhibit the personality traits we saw in the previous chapter, i.e. they are inclined to be extroverts, impulsive, and get bored easily. Whereas, people blinking more than the normal range have a faster internal clock and tend to have the opposite characteristics.

Recap

In summary, psychedelic drugs that stimulate brain neurotransmitters, like LSD, marijuana, magic mushrooms (psilocybin), amphetamines (speed), or mescaline, boost alertness and the speed of information processing and slow down time, while depressant drugs that suppress these neurotransmitters appear to speed time up. In this chapter, we saw how drugs like marijuana, cocaine, and LSD increase levels of dopamine in the brain and enhance concentration and feelings of wakefulness. Smart drugs and cognitive enhancers have a similar effect on alertness and attention and, undoubtedly, slow the experience of time by accelerating the brain's speed of processing information. Mental disorders, such as ADHD, Parkinson's, and Schizophrenia, are also characterized by abnormal levels of neurotransmitters and these patients experience similar distorted time perception.

In the first part of this book, we explored how we perceive time and the brain mechanisms involved in speeding it up or slowing it down. In the second part, we explored the factors that affect the perceived speed of time. These factors mainly affect the *prospective* time experience in the present, or what psychologists refer to as the experience of *"time-in-passing"*. We looked at the level of attention we devote to track time, our level of alertness and mental arousal, or going through life-threatening situations, our emotions and unique personality traits, as well as the influence of drugs and mind enhancers. All of these factors speed up or slow down the perceived flow of time by influencing the speed of our thoughts. That is, the speed at which we perceive reality. The effects are either a stretching or shrinking of the activity duration we are engaged in. It is all about the *'experienced duration'*, as it is unfolding *now*. But what about the experience of time in the past or in the future?

How do we perceive the duration of events that are already part of the past and which are later recalled? This could be a recollection of how long or short a vacation was, how long a meeting went on for, or how long a month or year seemed to last. The time interval that can be recalled could range from a few seconds to, in principle, a whole lifetime. Similarly, how do we anticipate the future and plan for things ahead of time? In the last part of the book, we will look in more depth at how we recall the duration of things we did in the past, and what causes those remembered events to stretch or shrink in our mind. This is essential to how we perceive the whole span of our life and vital to our sense of satisfaction and fulfillment. It will also help us understand how we experience time when planning and anticipating the future and why time speeds up as we grow older.

PART THREE

HOW DO WE PERCEIVE THE PAST AND THE FUTURE?

CHAPTER 10

A TIME TO REMEMBER

Time Perception and Memory

'Life can only be understood backwards, but must be lived
forwards'
— Soren Kierkegaard

Tin Box Memories

How is it that some people can clearly recall detailed memories from their
earliest childhood years, while most of us struggle to recover any
recollections from that time? We all yearn to remember the things we did,
the people we met, and the streets, houses, and playgrounds we grew up in.
After all, the tiniest details of those significant events are a big part of our
life story. But, as we grow older, that time fades away, as if it was never
part of our life. Those years are often distilled into only a few moments
worth of memories. If we had the chance to go back in time and relive it
one more time, we would surely seize that opportunity to save every
memory, every scrap of paper, every schoolbook, and every gift from a
friend, and every moment of laughter. That is obviously not possible.

However, as we shall see, brain scientists believe that our memories, though they may seem remote and ephemeral, are not lost but lie dormant deep inside our mind, waiting for the right moment when they are re-awakened.

One particular memory that has great significance is our first and earliest childhood memory. Try to remember it as vividly as you can. Where were you? What were you doing? Who was with you? What happened in that moment? According to the great Austrian psychologist Alfred Adler, your first memory is a window into the rest of your life and the cornerstone upon which you build the rest of your personal memories. As such, it reveals a lot about how you turned out to be. The event that makes up your earliest memory may not be remembered accurately and your mother may have told you that it did not really happen that way, but that makes no difference. What is important is how *you* remember it and what *you* believe was true. In fact, every time you remember something, you essentially recreate its details in your mind, slightly changing it in the process. Your memory is not like a hard disk that saves images that will look exactly the same each time you access them. Every time you recall an experience from your past, you reconstruct and relive it and, in doing so, you unconsciously alter its content for the better. If it was an unpleasant experience, you erase some of that negative sting and fill in the gaps with fabricated details. If it was a pleasant one, you add positive details to make it even more memorable and enjoyable. The result of such an emotional coping technique is that, when you look back over your life, you will likely perceive it to be more positive than negative.

Your unique memories are crucial in shaping who you are. Thus your identity depends partly on all of those events, people, and places you can recall. The way you experience your past also affects your present thoughts, feelings, and actions. On a fundamental level, you are what you remember. This is also true on a cultural level for a people as a whole. Those who share a common past also share a common identity and culture.

When we think back on our own past, we realize that it is made up of a series of mental snapshots starting from our earliest memories, through to the various defining moments in our life: the good and the bad, the happy and the sad, the mistakes we made, and the lessons we learned. We view our own lifetime and how long we have been living in terms of the number of unique memories that we have. The higher the number of memories, the longer we perceive our lifetime to be. It is, therefore, important to be able to remember those significant moments so that when we recall our past, we will be satisfied that we have lived a fulfilling life. Recalling a positive past is essential to our happiness and sense of well-being.

Locating the Past

The biggest problem with the past is that it is not easy to remember. First, you need to locate when an event has occurred in time. Then, you need to recall how long it took and what actually happened. Such assessments form the basis of many present decisions you make, even the relatively mundane ones. For instance, if you were trying to choose a restaurant for a dinner with your wife, you might want to know whether you had Japanese or Italian food more recently. In deciding what to wear, you may look in your closet to determine which of two shirts you wore longer ago. We are constantly trying to locate the timing and order of events from the past.

If you were trying to locate an object in a room, you would normally use visual information, such as your sense of direction and certain spatial reference points to determine if that object is to the left or right, or whether it is high or low. However, when we are trying to locate an event from the past, things are more difficult since we do not have a solid coordinate system that we can relate to. So how does our brain encode memories with time? How do we know which memories are of recent events and which are of events that were long ago?

Our internal time coordinates are based on patterns of time, i.e. hours, days, weeks, months and years. We are constantly aware of these cycles and we relate events to when they occur within them. There are also major milestones in our lives that we tend to use as fixed reference points, e.g. the year we graduated from school, the date on which we got married, or started our first job. These familiar time patterns and milestones form the basis of locating events from the past. Our brain reconstructs the timing of an event by estimating its distance from the present, by comparing it to familiar time patterns, or by associating it with events that directly succeed or precede it in time. We recall events from our memory by relating them to personal 'landmarks', such as "I was attending an annual party" or "It was within a few weeks of the birth of my first child" [131]. For example, you might recall that you got married in September 2001 (time location) which was 16 years ago (time distance), and that this was immediately after you joined a new company (relation to another event). This time information aids us in arranging our memories chronologically into an autobiographical story.

If you were an archeologist trying to establish the age of an ancient golden cup that had recently been found while digging in some old ruins, the first thing you would probably do would be to determine the time that has elapsed since that cup was made. You might use carbon-dating technique to determine the distance from the present and find that the cup was produced about 2,000 years ago. You might then search the cup's surroundings for some clues to reveal its location in time and the era it had belonged to. Lastly, the features on the cup itself, such as the carvings on its surface or the technology used to produce it, might give you a hint as to when it was created relative to other contextual information. In the same way, our brain uses information about distance from the present, location in time, and relative time of occurrence to arrange the order of our memories in time. Our brains locate events in the past by using time information extracted from the memory content itself. We use the context in which a memory is recalled to judge the time in which it occurred. For example, if it is winter now and you have a mental snapshot of yourself wearing a swimsuit on a beach, your brain will assume that this memory is older than another memory snapshot where you are in a ski resort wearing heavy winter clothes (unless you skied the winter before as well). Moreover, our brains store memories by the order in which they occur. As it stores new memories, it pushes older ones further into the past. The distance of an event from the present is therefore directly related to its memory trace. The strength of a memory fades with time, so a stronger memory trace is judged by our brain to be more recent than a weaker one. Also, the more details you can remember from an event, the more recent it will seem [132]. Last night's football game will seem more vivid than the game you saw last week. As time passes by, the unimportant details start to fade away, so that after, say a month, if you try to recall which game occurred first, you will guess that it is the one about which you remember the least detail.

Now try to remember the name of one of your Grade 3 teachers. You will find that a bit hard. How about any teacher from Grade 12? That is likely to be much easier to recall, since it is more recent. Now try recalling the name of any teacher from Grade 11 and keep going back until you reach Grade 3. By going backwards in time, grade by grade, you may slowly be able to remember your third grade teacher successfully. That is what researchers found at the State University of New York when 161 students were asked to recall the name of one schoolteacher from each Grade 1 to 12. Some had to do it backwards, i.e. Grade 12 to 1, while others did it forwards, i.e. from grade 1 to 12, and still others were asked to recall them randomly. The results indicated that students were faster and more accurate with their recollections when they started with Grade 12 and moved backwards, than when the teachers were recalled starting with Grade 1 going forward, or when remembered in a random order [133]. It turns out that backward search through long-term memory is more efficient than forward search. In the same way, if you try to recall what you did on your summer vacation four years ago, it will be easier if you started by listing the intervening vacations in backward order. The reason for why we tend to remember things better when looking backwards in time is that recent memories are more accessible than distant ones and the context of one successfully retrieved memory facilitates the recall of the adjacent one. Of course there are several other ways to remember the past. I will not go into more details here, for there are excellent books that focus on memory improvement and enhancement. However, I will just mention one quick example here. The best way, for instance, to remember your wedding anniversary or your wife's birthday is to forget it once. Rest assured, that will be the last time you forget it!

'Backward search through long-term memory is more efficient than forward search'

Remembered Durations

Trying to work out when events have occurred in the past is only half the problem. Another issue is remembering how long they took. But when we recall the duration of something we did in the past, what is it that we are really remembering?

One of the earliest, and most famous, answers to this question comes from St Augustine in his book '*The Confessions*' which contains a long and fascinating exploration of time and in which he raises the following conundrum: 'When we say that an interval of time is short or long, what is it that is being described as having a short or long duration? It cannot be what is past, since that has ceased to be, and what is non-existent cannot presently have any properties, such as being long. However, neither can it be what is present, for the present has no duration. In any case, while an event is still going on, its duration cannot be assessed' [134]. As you might have guessed, Augustine's answer to this puzzle is that, when we guess the duration of an event, what we are measuring is actually in our memory. From this, he concludes that past and future exist only in our mind and that our perception of an event's duration must somehow be related to an aspect of the memory from that event. So if you are trying to recall the duration of a movie you saw last night or how much time it took you to finish a report last week, the interval itself does not exist anymore; what is left of it is only a memory trace.

While engaged in such activities, you may not have been particularly aware of the passage of time and you only recall those durations after the fact. As we saw in Chapter 1, psychologists refer to this as '*retrospective time experience*' or 'remembered duration'. A 'remembered duration' can span an interval of a few seconds to, in principle, a whole lifetime. This is different from the 'experienced duration' (*prospective time experience*) that we explored in the previous chapters and which is related to the experience of time as it is passing 'now'. As we saw, the 'experienced duration' is influenced by factors such as our emotions, our alertness levels, the degree of attention or distraction we devote to time keeping, and also depends on some of our personality traits. In contrast, the 'remembered duration' only exists in our memory and, as we shall see, its duration is only influenced by the amount of memories we retain in our mind. This is why, in this chapter, you will note that some of the time perception factors that we already covered seem to have a counter effect on remembered durations compared to experienced durations. The remembered duration of a past event does not always match the experienced duration of the present and we will shortly see why such mismatches occur. Let us first look at what makes a remembered duration seem long or short.

We saw previously that the apparent speed of time is dependent on the brain's information processing speed, that is, how much information our mind can absorb and store in memory during a certain time interval. The more information there is, the longer a duration appears and the slower time seems to flow. A similar relationship exists between the information stored in our memory and the duration of remembered events. This has been explored by eminent psychologists and scientists since the 18th century, but it was psychologist Robert Ornstein who gave the research a great leap forward when he came up with the 'storage size hypothesis'. In the 1960s, Ornstein conducted a series of experiments to understand the connection between the amount of information stored in our memory and our sense of time [135]. In some experiments, he asked volunteers to inspect various paintings with varying degrees of complexity and then asked them to guess how long they spent examining the paintings. He found that those who saw the complex paintings estimated longer durations compared to those who saw the simpler ones. Similarly, he played tapes with various sounds on them and then asked the volunteers to estimate the duration for which they had been listening. He found that volunteers who listened to tapes with very dense sound information later estimated longer time durations compared to those who listened to tapes with very little sound on them. The conclusion is that the complexity and intensity of the information being processed and stored in the brain affects the perceived duration of remembered events. This is known as the 'storage size hypothesis' which states that when people are asked to recall the duration of something they did in the past, they examine the amount of memories stored from that period. The greater the number of snapshots and the more complex and intense the information being mentally processed, the greater the memory storage required and the longer that duration will seem.

Evidence for the role of memory in time perception comes from listening to music. What happens to time when you are listening to your favorite song? A couple of minutes of intent listening feels longer than usual. When it is over, it feels like time slowed down. I remember my early experience with classical music, when I got hooked on Wagner's Overture from 'The Mastersinger's of Nuremberg'. The piece is about 10 minutes long, but time appeared to halt with every note so that it felt like half an hour had passed when it was over. Wagner's orchestration is quite remarkable, with very complicated counterpoint melodies, layered on top of each other with colorful acoustic timbres, so the piece requires a lot of concentration in order to understand what is going on. It is also made up of several musical motifs that segment the piece into a complex sequence of memory markers. We saw previously how music also raises the alertness levels and causes the experienced duration to subjectively stretch as if the present has slowed down. Here, the level of complexity increases the amount of auditory information that is processed causing the remembered durations to expand in our mind when later recalled. Capturing and storing complex and novel information causes remembered durations to appear longer.

One possible reason for this has to do with the way the brain uses the concept of space to perceive time. Recall from Chapter 1 that we can only think about time in terms of space and distance, such as 'the meeting was *long*', or 'the weekend was *short*', or 'the war is *behind* us'. Due to this inextricable connection, our brain perceives time periods in the same way it perceives areas within a space. A well-known optical illusion reveals that a shape will appear larger when filled by a number of distinct elements than when it is empty [136]. In the same way, a time interval that is filled with intense mental activity that generates lots of memories will seem longer when later recalled than an empty interval of the same duration [137].

'Capturing and storing complex and novel information causes remembered durations to appear longer'

Likewise, when you are engaged in an activity that is segmented into several parts, the duration will appear longer than if the activity was one continuous chunk. To test this, researchers at Arizona State University prepared two kinds of tape recordings consisting of 27 nouns and the names of 3 U.S. presidents. Both recordings lasted 170 seconds. One recording was non-segmented and had all three presidents' names appear first followed by the 27 nouns. The second recording was segmented into three parts with the three presidents' names appearing in positions 10, 20, and 27. The researchers requested the students to estimate the duration of the recording and found that they judged the non-segmented recording to be shorter than the segmented one, even though both recordings were of the same duration. The reason is that segments create memory markers that are easily stored and retrieved later, so the segmented recording appeared longer. In short, remembered durations are a function of the quantity, complexity, and intensity of information processed during those intervals of time.

This has some significant real-life implications on how to control the subjective speed of time. When you have no choice but to go through routine or mundane activities (like doing your laundry or cleaning the house), you might want to get through it with no breaks or segmentation so as to create the least number of memory markers. Every time you stop for a break between chores, you remember the chores you have just done and think ahead to what you still have to do which makes it feel like they are taking all day. Whereas if you do them without a break, you do not reflect on what has come before or will come next and, with fewer memory markers, you will feel it is over quickly. On the other hand, if you are enjoying a fun activity or vacation and want to later remember that pleasant time as being long, you would want to segment it into smaller parts and savor every moment for the longest possible time. It is like eating a delicious chocolate cake, slowly and bit-by-bit so that it feels like it lasted longer. To recall your vacation as having lasted for a long time, you should mentally split it into smaller parts; the time you visited that landmark place, the time you had dinner in that special restaurant, and the water sport activity you did in the morning, and so on. Then you would store as many mental snapshots from those parts as you possibly can. This will help you create more memory markers in your mind that, in retrospect, will make your vacation seem longer than it really was.

'Remembered durations are a function of the quantity, complexity, and intensity of information processed during those intervals of time'

The combined remembered durations of past events affect how long you perceive last month, last year, or even the last decade to be. If, for instance, you feel that last year went by very quickly, it may be due to the lack of any significant memory markers or it could be that the memories that you actually collected during that year faded. You might initially recall rich memories, for instance, from the adventure you had on a recent camping trip. But, after a year, what is left of the trip in your mind does not amount to much more than a couple of mental snapshots. As years go by, the whole trip will barely leave a trace and might be completely forgotten. It is like you were never there. This is similar to our childhood memories that are gradually mostly lost, as if we never lived those first few years. The question, then, is whether there are ways to keep pleasant memories intact in our minds for longer, and whether there is a way that we can remember unpleasant times as being shorter than they actually were.

Maintaining Memories: Novelty and Routine

The key to maintaining memories lies with the degree of novelty. It is not only the quantity or complexity of mental snapshots that defines how we remember time intervals, but also how novel the captured information is. As confirmed by the great American Psychologist, William James, *"the awareness of change is the condition on which our perception of time's flow depends."* The change can be of any sort, from changes in the context to personal mood changes, or it could be in the form of new experiences and novel activities that create more memory markers. The perceived duration of a remembered event depends on the number of changes observed and recalled from memory. If the information within an interval of time is new and constantly varying, the brain will record more snapshots and that time interval will appear longer than it really is. When it is familiar and monotonous, the brain will perceive no change, record fewer snapshots, and that time interval will appear shorter.

This helps us understand why the duration of novel activities feels longer compared to the duration of routine ones. A typical example is a two-hour flight which might seem like four hours for someone who has never taken a plane, while it might seem like half an hour for a frequent flyer. This difference in time perception was confirmed by studies in which researchers found that people who routinely fly on planes felt safer and reported that time passed more quickly during flights than it did for the people who fly less often [138]. Or consider the mundane daily experience of commuting or driving back and forth from home to your workplace. You do it so regularly that the buildings, street signs, and landmarks became so familiar that they are no longer register in your memory. Your brain recorded these snapshots on the first couple of trips until the route back home became routine and, to conserve energy, is no longer interested in capturing those scenes. Driving becomes a subconscious 'auto-pilot' skill that requires minimal attention. Sometimes you suddenly find yourself in front of your house and don't recall how you got there. Contrast the daily commute to work with taking a trip to somewhere you have never been before. The trip duration will seem longer going there because of all the novelty and the excitement involved in visiting a new place. Because everything is new, your brain records all the details along the way and the trip appears to have taken longer when later recalled. This might sound counter to what we saw before on how monotonous activities seem to take longer, but that was in relation to our experience of present passing time. As we shall see shortly, the opposite effect is experienced when we look back and perceive that time retrospectively.

'A time period seems longer if remembered in detail and shorter if remembered only in outline'

If you ever wondered why your work week goes by very quickly, the answer lies in the level of novelty you have in your life. When going through a normal routine day, a lot of the familiar information you encounter passes without being stored in your brain and is quickly forgotten. A typical day might start at the same time every morning, eating the same breakfast, taking the same route to work, sitting behind a desk, and performing the same tasks you did yesterday. Your brain has already captured and processed those routine activities a hundred times before and does not need to process any new information or remember any specifics. Your brain is working on auto-pilot. Moreover, the familiar daily routine does not provide any memory markers for judging time. When that day is recalled, fewer events are remembered and the day appears to have passed very quickly. Days slip into months and then into years, and before you know it, you are about to celebrate your 40th birthday and *The Simpsons* is already on Season 27!

Now imagine another day at work, but this time it is being spent in a training seminar in a mountain ski resort. You will feel that special day to be longer than usual due to the increased brain alertness and all the novel experiences you encounter. When that day is later recalled, it will also be rich with new memories and original information that will make that day seem longer. Our brain tends to retrospectively shrink empty or routine minutes, hours, and days while expanding action-packed and interesting ones. If your life is now nothing but a constant routine, when you look back at those years they will seem short. Introducing novelty in your life will give you richer memories and make your life seem longer.

A study on how people feel about their vacations provides evidence for the role of novelty on time perception. People who were checking-out of a hotel after having enjoyed a 4-day vacation at a beach resort were asked to mentally divide their vacation into 3 equal parts: beginning, middle, and end, and then to assess which part seemed the shortest. Most participants reported the last part as being the shortest and the first part as the longest. The reason is that in the first couple of days, everything is new: the hotel, the pool, the guestroom. There are so many things to explore that serve as memory markers. But once people became acquainted with the holiday routine, fewer memories are captured and that period will seem shorter as the vacation becomes more familiar. Therefore, to make your vacation last longer, it would make sense to spread the 'new' experiences across the whole trip and always have something exciting to look forward to towards the end. In recalling the vacation later on, every part of it would have had its share of memories that will make it last longer in our mind.

One more thing to consider is that not all novel experiences are created equal. Novelty that involves active movement is more intense than passive novelty. Here is an example: spend one day on the couch watching TV, perhaps an entire season of something you have not seen before, so it contains a lot of novelty. Now spend one day exploring a new city on foot or on bike. Just physically moving through space without stopping. Which day feels longer in retrospect? Which day was fuller and richer? Even though both introduced novelty it was physical movement that injected intensity to the novel experiences and caused time to slow down in retrospect. This goes back to the types of fun we described in an earlier chapter and how active leisure can induce a mental state of flow that actually speeds up the experienced present time. While on a walking tour, you might be fully absorbed in the surroundings that the whole day passes without being aware how much time elapsed. However, at the end of the day, when that time is later recalled, you look back and feel you had breakfast ages ago. We will shortly look at some of these time distortions that result when we try to compare the experienced duration of the present with the remembered duration of the past. But the key point here is that novelty in active leisure tends to create more memories than passive novelty and will consequently stretch the remembered duration of an event to a greater extent.

Stretching the Past

If you have been through a rough period in your life and would like to recall that time as a brief moment, you will want to forget as many details and memories from that period as possible. By reducing the number of negative memories, our brain will judge that unpleasant period to be shorter in comparison with the good times we have had. Fortunately, evolution has equipped our brains with a coping mechanism that wipes away the negative aspects of bad memories and rebrands them in a more positive light. When you have a nightmare, your brain is effectively replaying a real-life negative experience but altering the memory to remove its sting. By intentionally rethinking what happened, you change the memory and fill the gaps with positive details. Over a period of time, the whole memory becomes harmless and is more or less forgotten. Other ways to deal with negative memories involve avoiding places or objects that trigger those memories. Psychologists also recommend focusing on what has been learnt from that negative experience and rebranding it as beneficial wisdom.

Conversely, if you want to remember a good time in your life as being long, you will need to capture as many memories and details from that period as you can. But having a perfect memory capable of recalling every small detail of our lives is sadly not possible. Evolution did not allow us such unlimited memory capacities because it is not critical to our survival. Squirrels, on the other hand, need to remember the location of vast quantities of nuts and have evolved a memory that is greater than our own. We humans will just have to be satisfied with an imperfect memory that causes important details to fade with time. In fact, our brains cannot remain efficient if we do not forget. Nevertheless and despite this inevitable limitation, there are still ways to keep those good times fresh in our minds.

One way is to use mental exercises that will improve your short-term and long-term memory capacities. Self-help books on how to improve your memory and develop a quicker way of retrieving information are readily available. It is also important to improve your emotional memory. This involves reliving how you felt at certain moments in the past. Were you happy, excited, proud, or overjoyed? It is not simply about recalling what happened but, more importantly, how you felt at that moment. One tip offered by neurologist, Richard Restak, is to reacquaint yourself with your emotions by writing a letter to your younger self. Let us say that you are now 40 years old. Start by finding a photo of yourself when you were almost 20 years old, half of your present age. Focus on it for a while including where it was taken and what you were doing. Then, imagine you are your 20-year old self and write a letter to your older self about the dreams you had, the things you wanted to achieve, your hopes and worries about the future. Follow that up with another letter from the present 'you' to your younger self, telling the younger 'you' all about their future, the things they will end up doing, and who they will grow up to be. By doing that simple exercise, you might discover feelings that you have not experienced in years or you might expose memories that were long forgotten.

Another way to preserve memories is by using social media, for example Facebook or Instagram. An exciting vacation that you took in some exotic place two years ago may have been rich with memories and mental snapshots. However, as memories fade with time, you can now remember only a couple of main events. But with social media, you can now store all those memories on a timeline and create snapshots from that vacation that can be recalled anytime and anywhere. You no longer have to rely on your imperfect brain to preserve those precious memories but can easily recollect every detail of that vacation by browsing your Facebook or Instagram page. That vacation will never lose any of its richness and will always seem long. In the past, you had to go through albums or scrapbooks of paper photographs, but social-networking websites have made it easier to record and recall your past in preserved timelines. In Facebook, you could pick a date at random and look at the photos of what happened on that date or in that year, the friends you were interacting with, the 'status updates' you were posting. You could relive the day your child was born, that Christmas gathering, that New Year party, your vacation to Paris, and even those mundane every day memories. All of this will help you maintain fresh memories of valuable moments in time that otherwise would have been forgotten. The richness of these memories will, when combined over long periods of time, stretch the months and years that make up your perceived life span and contribute to your overall life satisfaction.

To recap, our remembered durations depend on the amount, complexity, and intensity of memories stored from past events, as well as the degree of novelty and contextual change observed. The higher the number of snapshots in our memory, the longer the duration will seem when later recalled. The more novel and interesting the event, the more snapshots are stored and the longer that event appears to be, as if time slowed down. In contrast, the more familiar the event, the shorter that interval seems, as if time flew by. With this in mind, let us explore some psychological time distortions that we experience in our daily lives and some additional practical applications that will help us in making good times longer and bad times shorter.

Time Distortions: Contrasting Present Time with the Past

In trying to explain his grand Theory of Relativity, Albert Einstein was allegedly reported to have said, 'Sit with a pretty girl for an hour, and it seems like a minute. Sit on a hot stove for a minute, and it seems like an hour. That's relativity.' While this quote is almost certainly apocryphal, it nevertheless portrays quite accurately the kind of psychological distortions in the perceived speed of time that result from how our attention is devoted or distracted from the passage of time. However, there is another type of time distortion that occurs when we compare how long an activity seems to have lasted immediately after it has ended (prospectively), with how long it will seem to have lasted when we recall it a few days later (retrospectively). Let us look at a few examples.

Imagine you are at a corporate dinner, the same one we saw earlier in the book, where you are bored and constantly checking your watch. This attention to the passage of time will make it feel that it is passing excruciatingly slowly. Now imagine an exciting dinner party where you meet many interesting people and get so absorbed with the stories and entertaining discussions that you lose track of time and before you know it, it is already time to leave. A boring dinner party seems to drag while an interesting one races by. The time experience in both these examples is a prospective one. But what happens if we try to recall those two events a few days later? This retrospective time experience depends on the amount of memories we collected from that event. We will therefore judge the duration of the interesting dinner to be longer because more exciting and entertaining conversations and encounters took place, even though at the time, it felt like time flew. On the other hand, when we recall the boring dinner party a few days later, it will seem like it was shorter since there were barely any memories stored, even though it dragged at that time. We will then conclude that, in retrospect, the interesting party must have lasted longer than the boring one. As a result, our experience of time *during* the event is in conflict with our recollection *after* the event. The 'experienced duration' does not match the 'remembered duration' and that is the basis for time distortions which we experience almost every day.

We saw how the remembered duration of an event depended on the number of memories stored from that event. The higher the number of snapshots in our memory, the longer the remembered duration will seem. A filled time period seems to us to be longer than an empty one. Whereas, the duration experienced prospectively feels longer when attention is directed to the passage of time and it seems shorter when we are distracted from tracking time. In other words, in 'remembered durations' you count memories, whereas in 'experienced duration' you essentially count time. 'Psychological time distortions' occur when we attempt to compare an experienced duration with a remembered one and get contradictory results. William James was among the first to observe this in 1890 when he wrote, '...in general, a time filled with varied and interesting experiences seems short in passing but long as we look back. On the other hand, a tract of time empty of experiences seems long in passing but in retrospect short.'

'In remembered durations you count memories, whereas in experienced durations you essentially count time'

Imagine a situation where one person is asked to perform a difficult mental math problem, while another person is asked to perform a simple mental math problem, and still a third person is asked to do nothing, all for the same time interval. Before beginning the activity, all 3 people are informed that they will have to guess how long it will take after completion. What would be the outcome? Research has confirmed that the activity will be estimated to be longest by the person doing nothing [139]. It will be estimated to be the shortest by the one doing the complicated mental math problem. For the person doing the simple math problem, it will be somewhere in between. Since all three people have to keep track of time while doing their activity, the person doing nothing can afford to allocate most of his attention to the passing time and will guess the longest and most accurate duration. The person doing the difficult math task will be focusing on solving the math problem and will lose track of time, so he will experience the shortest duration. The more we pay attention to time, the longer it seems and the slower it appears to run. Now, if this experiment was repeated but the participants were not told in advance that they would have to guess the activity's duration, so they would not have to pay attention to the passage of time, the opposite results would be obtained. If asked, after the task, how long it lasted, the person solving the complex math problem would guess at the longest duration as they would store more information in their memory from that activity. Whereas the person doing nothing at all would have virtually nothing to remember from that time and would recall the duration as very short [140].

Another interesting 2005 study conducted in Manchester, grandly-titled the 'Armageddon Experiment', illustrated the contradictory results between experienced and remembered durations. In that study, one group of people watched nine minutes of the action movie '*Armageddon*' while another group waited for nine minutes in an adjacent room. When the nine minutes were over, they were each asked to guess how quickly time seemed to pass. The people in the waiting room judged the time as having passed more slowly than the 'Armageddon' movie group who felt that time flew. The 'Armageddon' group were having more fun and, as we know, time flies when we are having fun. For the waiting group, the nine-minute waiting period felt longer since waiting involves a higher awareness of time compared to watching the movie which distracts attention from tracking time. After that, the participants where then asked to read a novel for 10 minutes, after which they were asked again to guess the time interval spent watching the movie or waiting. As expected, judging the time interval from memory led to opposite results; the waiting period was now perceived to be shorter than the 'Armageddon' period. This is because the waiting period was devoid of any interesting memories compared to the rich details stored by the movie group. In retrospect, the fewer number of memories from the waiting period caused the time interval to seem shorter compared to the movie group who recalled more memory markers causing the 9-minute time interval to feel longer [141].

This is similar to when we fall ill for a few days and feel time going very slowly with nothing much to distract our attention from the passage of time. However, once we recover, we look back retrospectively at those days and feel like they went by in a flash. That is because nothing remarkable happened. No novelty, no variation, and very few memory markers were encoded in our brain. The 'experienced duration' of a few ill days equates to a few hours of 'remembered duration' in our memory and,

$ /
1.00

Sell your books at sellbackyourBook.com!

Go to sellbackyourBook.com and get an instant price quote. We even pay the shipping - see what your old books are worth today!

Inspected

0002 1967846

7846   G

0002196

as time goes by, the whole period may be totally forgotten. Similarly, a stay at home parent's typical day is full of repeated tasks, from feeding the baby, changing diapers, bathing them, reading a bedtime story, etc. At the end of a long and hectic day, it seems like they had breakfast ages ago. The weekend finally comes and when they look back at the week, it seems like it flew because, except for the scarce first crawl, first walk, first word memories that occur over longer time period, the repetitive daily routine does not provide any significant memory markers.

In brief, 'experienced durations' depend on the level of attention dedicated to time while engaged in an activity, while 'remembered durations' rely on the number of memories that are later recalled. Time flies when you're having fun, but that duration will seem longer when recalled a few days later. In contrast, time drags when you are bored but will feel shorter when later recalled. As we shall see next, this type of time distortion is most pronounced during vacations.

The Holiday Paradox

The most commonly reported time distortion is vacation time. Imagine you are planning your next hard-earned vacation and you want it to last as long as possible. It is a short two-week vacation, but you want time to run as slowly as possible. You know that this can be done by increasing your level of alertness and focused attention so that your brain can process as much information and record as many mental snapshots as it possibly can. Researchers have estimated that a normal routine week would contain between three to four memories that are worth remembering. But when on vacation, the number of interesting memories can jump to as much as nine in one single day, depending on the type of vacation you take. Therefore, a day on vacation feels much longer retrospectively than a normal routine day. If, for instance, you decide to go to an entirely new place where you can experience a new culture, exciting adventures, taste new foods, listen to novel music, observe new sights and sounds, there will be many opportunities to retain memorable moments which will stretch the remembered duration. But during the vacation, you will be so absorbed with these novel experiences that your attention will be distracted from the passing time. As soon as it is over, the vacation feels like it was over in a flash. It is only when you return to work and later recall that vacation that you realize that there was so much novelty to chew on, so much information to record and process, and so many memories to keep, that makes it seem longer, as if time has stretched. The remembered duration will seem longer than the vacation duration that was experienced at that time.

If, on the other hand, you decide to take your two-week vacation to a familiar beach resort, the opposite time distortion occurs. You might spend the whole time in a relaxing mood, lying on the beach, reading a book, or enjoying the sun. The same ritual is repeated each day, with the exception of a nice dinner here and a short trip there. Having escaped your work environment and all its distractions, you are now able to devote your full attention to that peaceful rest time, and as a result, the days drag and the passing time slows down. However, when you are back to work and try to recall that vacation later, having collected only a few interesting memories, it will seem short. That experience might have been rejuvenating, but the vacation will not register much time in your mind. You will experience a time distortion, as the remembered duration feels shorter than the duration you experienced at that time. This takes us back to the topic of time spent in relaxation versus active leisure time and the degree to which each influence our present and past time experience. In passive leisure, attention to the passing time is greater so time slows down prospectively. However, that period will shrink retrospectively due to the reduced number of memory markers. In contrast, time flies in active leisure as we enter a state of flow and are distracted from the passing time. But that stretches the remembered past as more life-fulfilling memories are created.

In brief, the speed at which your vacation will pass depends on the type of holiday you go on. When that vacation is over and you try to recall it after a few weeks, it will seem long if it was adventurous or filled with novel experiences. Whereas, your vacation will seem short in retrospect, if it was spent in some familiar tourist resort, and it will later be recalled as if it was over in a flash.

This effect does not just apply to vacations and daily activities but can be used to enhance our overall perception of a more fulfilling life experience. If you want your life to seem long, you can slow it down by filling your weekends, months, and years with novel experiences. To have richer memories, you will also need an alert brain that can efficiently capture and retrieve them. But even with the best brain in the world, living your days to a routine will not provide it with any interesting material to absorb. The effect of memories on stretching the past time experience is also important because it counters the present time-speeding effect when having fun. Our retrospective time perception depends on the memories we collect when we are engaged in flow-inducing activities. We normally collect exciting memories during 'flow' experiences where time runs fast, but their large number and intensity produces a remembered past that is stretched. The more absorbed we are in these flow-inducing activities, the faster time runs in the present, but the more memories are captured and the longer that period will seem later on. Thus having fun makes for a satisfying present time experience but, more importantly, creates vivid and long-term memories which, when later recalled, will weave a rich mosaic that stretches the story of our life.

Let us now move away from the past and explore the ways we experience the future time, how we anticipate it, plan for it, and try to take some control over it as we grow older.

CHAPTER 11

MENTAL TIME TRAVEL

Perceiving the Future

'The timeless in you is aware of life's timelessness. And
knows that yesterday is but today's memory and tomorrow
is but today's dream'
— Gibran Khalil Gibran, 'The Prophet'

Time Travel?

Ever since humans developed the first hints of intelligence, they dreamt of
time travel, whether going back into the past to change what has occurred
or traveling to the future to alter what is about to happen. Unfortunately,
this is impossible except in science fiction movies. But it can be achieved
in our minds through mental time travel. The process by which we imagine
the future and then adjust our behavior to bring it about is one of the most
fascinating skills we possess. Our ability to travel mentally into the future
is possibly the crowning achievement of the human intellect.

   We are not the only species capable of future thinking. Scientists have
observed a primitive form of mental time travel behavior in some animals,

such as chimps and jaybirds. In 2009, zoo keepers at Furuvik zoo, in Sweden, reported that Santino, a male chimpanzee, had planned to hurl hundreds of stones at visitors to the zoo. They noticed that the chimp had been calmly amassing piles of stones in a place that faces the crowds, putting them into neat piles, apparently saving them to later throw at visitors when the zoo opened, as part of an aggressive display of dominance. After a few stones have been thrown with near-misses, researchers studying the phenomena suggested that Santino's behavior indicated forward planning and premeditated trickery. Similar behavior has been observed in birds. In one study, researchers housed some jaybirds on alternate days in two different houses: one day in a house where they received food, the 'breakfast' house, and the next day in a house where they received no food, the 'no breakfast' house. After a few days of alternating between the two houses, they were given a lot of extra food placed in a location where they could access both the 'breakfast' and 'no breakfast' houses. The researchers found that the birds started storing the surplus food in the 'no breakfast' house. This indicated that the birds anticipated that they would be hungry the next day and planned ahead by storing some of the surplus food in the 'no breakfast house'!

Such rudimentary planning abilities are obviously nothing compared to the human capacity to think ahead into the far future, imagine various potential scenarios, and envision the actions that are required to achieve a future outcome. Moreover, our mental time travel does not always have to be into the future. We can also time travel back to the past, replay a sequence of events that have already occurred, and construct all kind of hypothetical scenarios in our minds. We may replay an argument we had with a friend a few days ago to figure out what went wrong or what might have been done differently. But time travel into the future is more frequent. If you are unoccupied and sitting around with some free time, check your thoughts and you will find that your mind has automatically wandered into the future. That little voice inside your head is constantly talking to you about what to do next. You might be thinking about making a nice cup of coffee, or maybe calling a friend and planning lunch, or considering ordering some home delivery, or maybe getting some groceries and cooking at home. That constant chatter inside your mind is mostly about the future. In fact, scientists believe that people think about the future about 59 times each day, that is almost once every 15 minutes [142]. It appears that future thinking is our brain's default mode of operation.

Since no one can really see into the future, we have no choice but to use our imagination to envision how things might turn out to be or how we would like them to be. When we imagine ourselves in the future, we start from our present point in time and envision the various steps and tasks that we will be taking to reach that future situation. This is called 'mental simulation' and is actually a great technique for remembering things. When you develop a detailed mental image of something you plan to do in the future, you are more likely to remember to do it. If, for instance, you want to remember to pass by the dry cleaners to pick up your laundry, you can imagine yourself going to the shop, giving them your receipt at the reception, receiving your clothes, and paying at the counter. This method is far superior than repeating to yourself that you need to pass by the laundry shop. In the process of imaging the various steps you will take, you might think of other opportunities that you might otherwise have missed. Perhaps you could pass by the post office next to the laundry shop to post that letter, or go to the bank across the street to pay your utility bills. But how does our brain experience the future?

Imagine receiving an invitation for dinner next week to a new restaurant that you have never visited before and with a group of people you have never met. Imagine what the restaurant will look like, what decorations are on the wall, the chairs, the tables, etc. Imagine the people you are going to meet, the clothes they are wearing, imagine the food you will be eating, the drinks, and the dessert. If you look closely enough, you will realize that a lot of the details you came up with did not just appear from thin air, but are actual images from your past memories. We all use details from our past to imagine the future. Our memories constitute the building blocks for our future thinking. This is confirmed by studies performed on people who were asked to think about the future while connected to an fMRI brain scan. The results revealed that a small area of the brain called the hippocampus lit up, the very same area where memories are stored [143]. Other evidence comes from people who lose their memories. The famous case of Henry Molaison, known by thousands of psychology students as 'HM', who in 1953 lost his memory on an operating table in a hospital in Hartford, and who forms the basis of the main character in the movie *Memento,* cannot remember anything that happened more than a few minutes ago. Meaningfully, not only can he not recall the past, he cannot envision the future. When researchers ask him to picture himself somewhere he might go, he only sees a big emptiness.

Imagining the future is the mirror image of remembering the past. 'The present defines the future. The future builds on the foundation of the past,' says Lailah Gifty Akita, author of *Think Great: Be Great!* In both cases, we project ourselves into a mentally simulated scenario. Both processes are carried out by the same brain system. The more detailed the memories we carry, the better we are at planning the future. That is why elderly people or those with Alzheimer's have difficulties planning ahead. It becomes more difficult to remember the past, but it also becomes harder to imagine the future. In the same way that it is harder to remember an event that is far in the distant past compared to a more recent one, it becomes harder to imagine an outcome that is further into the future.

From an evolutionary perspective, we developed the capacity for mental time travel because it gave our ancestors an important advantage for survival. It allows us to anticipate the future based on past experiences so we can better plan ahead and be prepared for the unexpected. In fact, one of the main reasons our brains developed the ability to store past memories was to use them as lessons learnt for constructing future scenarios. We tend to think of memory as something that has to do with the past, but in reality, its main purpose has to do with the future. It is a tool used by the brain to generate simulations of potential future scenarios, giving us an edge in our struggle for survival. This capacity to travel in time mentally may be at the core of how we developed the concept of time. The ability to recall the past, which we saw earlier, and anticipate for the future, which we will explore now, eventually formed the basis of our time experience.

Time Distortions Created by Anticipation

You are watching your favorite football team playing the last 5 minutes of the World Cup final, having already scored 1 − 0. The opposing team is pressing hard and you obviously want those last five minutes to pass by quickly before they get the chance to equalize the score. But time crawls by agonizingly slowly as you eagerly anticipate that final whistle. Now, let us assume it is the other way round, and your team was down 0 - 1 in those last five minutes. You would be wishing those last minutes to stretch for as long as possible in order to postpone the final whistle, giving your team a chance to score. But instead, those last five minutes will feel so short and your team is racing against the clock as time flies. When it comes to our experience of the future, anticipating a pleasant event slows down time while dreading an unpleasant one speeds it up. These are situations we have all experienced in our life in a variety of ways.

When you are waiting for something to happen and feel that it is taking too long, this is normally the result of three related factors; the actual duration of what you are waiting for, how you feel about it, and whether you think that event is approaching or receding away from you. Obviously, there is little you can do about the first factor, but you can change how you feel about that future event and whether it is approaching or not. By controlling the last two factors, you can shorten long periods of boredom and extend delightful moments of happiness. An example will illustrate how our future outlook affects our perceived speed of time.

Imagine you are the manager of a prominent 5-star hotel and your employer has just offered you a big promotion that requires you moving to a famous remote island resort to manage their luxury hotel, with a huge uplift to your salary package and benefits. The planned move is expected in two months' time. It is the moment you have always been dreaming of and you start contemplating all the gains in that move, like the great weather, the career fulfillment, and all the things you can do with your additional income. However, your partner might have a different view on things. The move may represent a painful departure from home, family, or long-established friends, and she or he will instead start focusing on what will be lost. It is perceived as a gain or loss depending on each person's perspective and priorities. Consequently, the two months leading to the move will be perceived differently depending on the expected outcome. For you, the time leading to the move will seem to take forever. While for your partner, they want the time to stretch for as long as possible, but it will be over quickly. Studies have confirmed that future events that are expected to end with a loss appear to arrive faster than usual, compared to future events expected to end with a gain [144]. But what is the reason for that?

'Positive anticipation slows down time. Dread speeds it up'

One possible explanation for this time distortion has to do with loss aversion, which is people's tendency to prefer avoiding losses to acquiring gains. For most people, losing $100 feels more painful than gaining $100 feels good. Losses often 'loom larger' than gains. Recall in previous chapters how time and space are related in our mind because share the same brain circuitry. It is a fact that our visual system operates in such a way that when an object is large in size, our brain assumes it is near and when it is small, the brain assumes it is far. Similarly, since a loss looms larger than a gain, the event leading to that loss will appear nearer in time [144]. This was confirmed in 2010 at the Washington University in St. Louis in an experiment that involved 109 undergraduate students. Participants were asked to imagine that they were moving into a new office in two months. Some participants were told the new office is much larger and has more windows than their current office (considered a gain) and some were told the opposite (considered a loss). They were then asked how long will the time to move seem to them. The results indicated that the 2 months interval leading to the anticipated loss appeared shorter compared to the students anticipating a gain, as if time was running faster [144].

In a similar experiment, participants were randomly split into two groups: the 'gain group' were asked to imagine that their employer currently provided them with old Motorola phones and the 'loss group' were told their employer currently provided them with iPhones. All participants were then told that their company decided to standardize employee phones to streamline communication and that new phones would be distributed in two months. Participants in the 'gain group' learned that the new phone would be the more advanced iPhone, whereas participants in the 'loss group' learned that it would be the less advanced Motorola. They were then asked how long the time interval until the phone replacement seemed and the participants receiving a worse phone felt the interval until the exchange as shorter.

This time-distorting effect may be purely evolutionary in nature. During our human evolution, whenever we were in danger, it would have been more advantageous to assume that the threat was closer than it really was, just to be on the safe side. If you were one of our caveman ancestors and heard a rustling in the bush, it would be safer to assume that a lion is stealthily closing on you and about to eat you than to merrily keep going your way and assume the lion is too far to catch you (and end up being eaten)! If you exaggerate the proximity of danger, you will be able to defend more efficiently, in case the threat turns out to be real. Therefore, evolution has wired our brains in such a way as to instinctively perceive a potential loss as nearer in time than a gain, which explains why time feels like running faster when anticipating a loss. This brings us to the other major factor that influences our experience of the future that is how we see ourselves in relation to time.

Time and space are intricately related in our mind. We used that relationship to explain why 'empty durations', like empty rooms, appear shorter than 'filled durations'. The space-time relationship is also useful in explaining the motion of temporal events in time. As we saw in chapter 1, when we think of Christmas or the weekend as 'fast approaching', we perceive future anticipated events as moving towards us in time. But our emotions play an additional role in affecting how we see ourselves in relation to time. It is normal to approach the things that we like and move away from the things we dislike. When we desire something, we are attracted to it but when we fear something, our instinct is to withdraw. We do the same thing when it comes to approaching temporal events. This is how we psychologically manage the distance between us and pleasant or unpleasant events [145]. If we are looking forward to a pleasant event, like a wedding or graduation day, we will see ourselves as moving towards that event, as in the ego-moving metaphor, that we saw in chapter 1. We are on a direct collision course with that event. We will naturally be more alert and excited and this boosts the speed of processing information and the speed of our internal clock, so that the perceived duration stretches and time seems to slow down. Furthermore, because the anticipated event is seen as a gain, we will be eager for it to occur sooner rather than later and will focus more on the time leading up to it. As a result, that additional attention we devote to the passing time will make the waiting period seem longer. Time drags when we anticipate Christmas or the weekend arrival. Such pleasant anticipated events always appear further in the future than they really are. Positive anticipation draws our attention to time and causes it to run slowly. In contrast, time speeds up when we are dreading a negative outcome. If we are worried about a future event, like a surgical operation or a dentist appointment, we would naturally see ourselves standing still, or even running away, as the negative event approaches us. We are more focused on the event and less on the time leading up to it. This inattention to the passing time causes it to pass swiftly and the dreaded event arrives faster than we hoped for.

In brief, how we feel about the future affects our perception of time. Emotions that come from anticipating pleasant or unpleasant events can change the way we think about time and how it is moving in relation to us. Our experience of the future is influenced by how desirable the anticipated events are. When the future outlook is positive, time slows down and when it is negative, time speeds up. A practical tip to take here is that if you want to slow down time, you should always try to create pleasant anticipation in your life. When you imagine something wonderful is going to happen in the future, you create hope and excitement, both of which can make the present slow down and make it even more pleasant. We will later see that you can sometimes derive more pleasure from anticipating a pleasant event than the actual event itself. Similarly, experiencing negative feelings when dreading an unpleasant future event can sometimes be worse than when the event actually occurs.

Time and Expectations

Our expectations of when things will get done can create mixed feelings too, and these also affect our perception of time. We live in a society that is ruled by fairly rigid time schedules, such as planned appointments, the start of TV programs, and schedules for public transport systems. We look at our watch and can tell how much time we have until the next train arrives or how long until the next meeting starts. We know how much time needs to be spent on certain activities and can predict when they should be completed so we can move on to other things. In most situations, the duration of these events occur in line with our expectations. But, in some cases, we become upset that the anticipated event is taking longer than expected, or we may be pleasantly surprised that it took less time to come around than originally anticipated. Researcher found that the experienced speed of time depends on how our expectations are met. For example, you are ordering fast-food at a restaurant and the service counter informs you that, due to a technical problem in the kitchen, your food will be ready in 10 minutes when it usually only takes two. Because your expectations were not met, those 10 minutes will feel longer than they really are. In contrast, let us say you have regular appointments with your doctor where you have to arrive 30 minutes ahead of the appointment before he can take you in. However, on that particular day, a patient did not show up and, to your surprise, the assistant informed you that the waiting time is only 10 minutes. Because your expectation has been positively exceeded, those 10 minutes will pass very quickly. The same 10-minute duration feels differently depending on how your expectation was met.

Or imagine you are waiting to pick up a friend from the airport and his flight is expected to land in 10 minutes. However, due to poor weather conditions, the Flight Display Screen changes to indicate a 25-minute delay in arrival. Those extra 15 minutes you now have to wait will pass extremely slowly. If it was the other way round, say you arrived 30 minutes early to the airport and set your expectations for that waiting time. However, for some reason, the Flight Display Screen indicates that the plane is landing in just 15 minutes. You will be pleasantly surprised and those 15 minutes will pass fairly quickly. In both cases, you actually waited for exactly 15 minutes. However, depending on how your expectations were met, those 15 minutes felt longer in the first scenario and shorter in the second.

One thing to take from this is that when you have to wait, lowering your expectations about when things will get done will make your waiting time shorter and more pleasant. You will face fewer disappointments and you will be pleasantly surprised if it ends up taking less time. Change the way you look at waiting time. We are all more than happy to take a 10-

minute break at work but feel we are wasting time when we have to wait 10 minutes in a queue.

'Lowering your expectations about when things will get done will make your waiting time experience more pleasant'

The Optimistic Future

When we think about our past, we get mixed emotions. There are some 'highs' and some 'lows', warm memories and some bad ones. Nevertheless, we are mostly stuck with memories of the events that have already occurred, even though we tend to reconstruct them in a more positive way. In contrast, when we think about the future, we are free to imagine any scenario or outcome that we like and it tends to be optimistically biased. Research has shown that we all have a natural tendency to envision a positive future. It is what causes smokers to believe that they are less likely to contract lung cancer than other smokers. One reason for that positive bias is it is easier and nicer to imagine. You can, for instance, easily imagine yourself driving a nice Ferrari but it will be much harder to imagine yourself in a hospital after crashing it. Positive outcomes makes us feel good and are therefore desirable, whereas negative outcomes involve more intense emotions that are more difficult to summon and are to be avoided.

Our natural tendency to be optimistic about the future has many beneficial effects. When you think positively you will persevere in the face of difficulties and will not give in easily. Your mind will be open to creative thinking and will be better at solving problems. With a positive attitude, you are emotionally better prepared to cope with failure, even when you aim for higher aspirations. Optimistic thinking is also beneficial to your mental and physical health. People who think positively about the future tend to be less susceptible to depression, alcoholism, and obesity. There is also evidence that the immune system is much more effective in fighting disease when the attitude is positive and recovery from illness is faster too. This was confirmed in a study showing how optimistic patients recovered faster after coronary artery bypass surgery and returned to full-time work earlier than patients with a more pessimistic outlook [146].

However, not all future thinking is beneficial. Take, for instance, self-help books that emphasize fantasies for achieving personal goals. The widely popular book *The Secret* by Rhonda Byrne, is a typical example that is based on the superstitious 'Law of Attraction' and claims that imagining a future positive outcome can create life-changing results, such as increased wealth, health, and happiness. According to that approach, simply imagining an outcome will somehow cause it to occur. If you want to be a successful businessman, all you have to do is imagine yourself in that role and it will be yours. If you want to lose weight, simply imagine that you have already lost weight and the universe will somehow conspire to fulfill your desires. Another example is the book '*Visualization for Change*' by Patrick Fanning which claims that in order to become rich, all you need is to imagine all the things you would do when you are rich. You should see yourself enjoying your favorite activities, surrounded by loved ones and friends, popular and relaxed, wearing new stylish clothes, driving a new car, and playing with a new tennis racquet [147]. The claim is that if you fantasize about these things, your positive thinking will attract them and the universe will devise a way to make them yours!

While all of that sounds fantastic, it is far from true. The universe does not know that you exist, does not care that you exist, and is not really interested about your desires. No matter how hard you think about something, it will not be yours if you do not do anything about it. Having optimistic expectations is very different from having positive fantasies. Convincing someone that pure fantasies can change their reality is not just harmless wishful thinking, it can be detrimental. First, there is no scientific evidence supporting the amazing claims of the 'law of attraction'. Simply imagining a favorable future outcome does not create the circumstances for that outcome to happen. If that was true, people would stay young forever and no one would ever get sick, grow old, or die. But we all know that ageing and death are not optional. Likewise, if you can get a nice Ferrari car by just imagining it in your future, then why is everyone not driving expensive cars? Why are millions of people still dying of starvation? Can they not imagine a nice home delivery meal magically appearing in their house? Positive fantasies are very nice, but they do not change the basic fact that you simply cannot get something out of nothing.

Fantasies and Positive Expectations

There are, therefore, two different ways of thinking about the future; the first as a positive expectation and the second as a pure fantasy. Each has a different effect on your motivation and the action you will eventually take. When you imagine your successes, you visualize them in your mind and use past memories to create mental images of the anticipated future outcome. Expectations are more grounded in reality as they rely on past experiences. You expect to do well in an exam because you did well in previous exams. You expect to find a new job because you always managed to find a good job in the past. Having high expectations of success increases your motivation to act. In contrast, daydreaming creates fantasies that help you escape reality. Fantasies involve imagining something you hope will happen in the future, but are not experiencing right now. You fantasize about having achieved success and start consuming its rewards, which in turn reduces your motivation to work harder to succeed.

> **'Positive fantasies are very nice, but they do not change the basic fact that you simply cannot get something out of nothing'**

In a fantasy, you start experiencing a very bright and joyful future, ahead of time. As a result, you do not feel that you need to act and you will easily overlook the difficulties that you might face in realizing that fantasy. You will, therefore, not be motivated to focus on an action plan and this lack of mental rehearsal reduces your chances of success. Research has found that people who fantasize about an idealized future will very likely face depression. In contrast, positive expectations focus more on the process and actions needed to achieve success. It might not be pleasant to think about the problems you will face, but this kind of future thinking fosters the key ingredients for successful attainment. This was demonstrated in a study conducted at the University of California with 77 students who were recruited one week before their midterm exam. One group of students was told to focus on the outcome and imagine that they already received a grade A on the exam. They were told to 'see themselves standing in front of the glass case where the midterm exam grades are posted, holding their breath, moving their gaze horizontally to find their score, learning that they had received an A, beaming with joy, and feeling confident and proud'. Another group of students were told to focus on the process and 'visualize themselves studying for the exam in a way that would lead them to obtain a grade A'. They would see themselves studying, sitting at their desks, on their beds, or at the library, and studying the chapters, eliminating distractions. All students practiced this mental simulation for 5 minutes daily for about a week before the exam date. After the exam, the results were clear; the students who focused on the process and imagined the steps required to pass the exam obtained higher grades than those students who focused on the outcome and imagined they had already passed the exam [148].

In brief, optimistic future thinking is beneficial when it is put into action through high expectations, rather than unrealistic expectations. It helps us achieve the goals we desire whereas positive fantasies and wishful thinking, as described in self-help books, are a hindrance. Future thinking is more effective in achieving a target goal when we imagine the process and steps we need to take to reach that desired outcome, rather than focusing on the outcome itself. This is because when we imagine the process of attaining a goal, our mind starts problem-solving and creates a more realistic expectation of the end result. This translates into motivation and a plan of action that will achieve the desired goal. Now a key aspect of any plan is the ability to predict when future events will happen and how much time is required to complete future tasks. Whether we are planning the rest of our day or committing to a deadline at work, our ability to predict how long things will take is a critical skill. Planning is another important aspect of the way we experience future time.

The Planning Fallacy

Have you missed an appointment because you misjudged the travel time it takes to get you there? Have you ever renovated your home and realized it was taking longer than originally anticipated? Have you taken lots of office work home intending to complete it over the weekend, knowing that you haven't completed much on previous weekends, only to return most of it back to the office again? Do you predict that you can complete tasks, such as submitting a term paper or returning tax forms, well before the deadline when you know that in the past similar projects were finished very close to the deadline? If that sounds all too familiar, then welcome to the 'planning fallacy'.

The planning fallacy was first proposed by Daniel Kahneman and Amos Tversky in 1979. It is essentially a biased internal conviction that a current project will go as well as planned, even though similar projects from the past have failed to fulfill their planned outcomes. The future is perceived to be rosier than the past. Lessons from the past fade from our attention in light of optimistic plans about the future. Research has shown that people, on average, underestimate how long it takes to do things by a significant 40 percent! [149] In 1974, during the oil crisis that hit the U.S., a study conducted on drivers waiting in line to buy gasoline found that most drivers underestimated the length of time they expected to wait and the underestimation increased the further away the driver was from the beginning of the line. In a 1994 study, 37 psychology students at the University of Waterloo, Ontario, were asked to estimate how long it would take to finish their senior theses. The average estimate was around 34 days. They were also asked to estimate how long it would take "if everything went as well as it possibly could" and the average response was 27 days. Finally, they were asked to estimate how long it would take "if everything went as poorly as it possibly could", and the average response was 49 days. After the students completed their theses, researchers found that the average actual completion time was 56 days! Only 30 percent of the students managed to complete their thesis in the amount of time they originally predicted [150]. We all simply underestimate how long a task will take.

This optimistic bias in future thinking applies to major construction projects as well. The famous example is the Sydney Opera House, which in 1957 was originally planned to be completed by 1963 at a cost of $7 million. It was actually completed ten years behind schedule and at a cost of $102 million. The Channel Tunnel connecting Britain and France was due to open between London and Paris in June 1993, with a budget of 2.6 billion pounds. The real cost ended up being 4.6 billion pounds, and it was formally opened in May 1994. A building can be completed on time, if there are no delays to the delivery of material, labor strikes, severe weather conditions, funding problems, last minute design changes, or a host of other unforeseeable delays for which no provisions are considered. The probability that at least one of these factors will occur is greater than people normally expect. In my real estate development and project management career, I have seen that happen far too often. We are not only optimistic about how the future will turn out, but we also tend to be very optimistic in our predictions of the time required to complete future tasks, even though we know that similar tasks have taken longer than planned in the past. The planning fallacy is at the root of many of our hopes, fears, and disappointments. It is the main reason why many people are chronically late to meetings or cannot consistently meet deadlines. It is therefore important to understand how it works.

One reason why we tend to construct an optimistic scenario of when a task will be completed is that we tend to ignore the memories of how long similar tasks have taken in the past. When we focus on future plans, we construct in our imagination a story about how we will achieve our goal, and by doing that we forget to consult our past. We tend to neglect the results of similar plans from the past because prediction is, by its very nature, a focus on the future rather than on the past. This future orientation prevents us from looking back. We normally think of planning as the process of developing a series of steps that have a clear start, and which take into consideration the specific features about a project that will eventually lead to a successful conclusion of that project. This is called the narrow 'inside' view of predicting the time to achieve a future goal. In contrast, the 'outside view' is when you deliberately avoid planning the various steps you need to complete your project and just consider how long it took to finish similar projects in the past. This sounds counterintuitive since the 'inside' view is supposed to be more detailed and should give more accurate predictions. Both views are essential, however, research has shown that predictions are more accurate when you put more weight on the 'outside' view, i.e. past results.

At the Wilfrid Laurier University in Waterloo Ontario, researchers wanted to test the anecdote that people are always late in their Christmas shopping. A group of undergraduates were asked to describe highly specific plans for their Christmas shopping - where, when, and how- while another group was simply asked when they expected to finish their Christmas shopping, based on previous experience and without any shopping plans. On average, the first group optimistically expected to finish shopping more than a week before Christmas, whereas the group that made no plans estimated they would get it done four days before Christmas, at the latest. Both groups actually finished, on average, three days before Christmas, which demonstrates that that group that did not think of a plan and relied on past experience had the more accurate predictions [151].

Another possible cause for this optimistic planning bias has to do with our future time perspective. Imagine yourself sun tanning on a nice sandy beach, sipping a cold drink or reading a book. Do you see yourself looking at the sea from inside your skin? Or do you see your body lying on the sand from an outside point of view? When we think about the future, we generally adopt one of these two visual perspectives: the first-person perspective where you imagine things unfolding as if you were actually carrying them out, or the third-person perspective, in which you see yourself from outside performing the events as they unfold from an observer's point of view. In the first-person perspective, you are actually acting the future scenario in your mind, while in the third-person perspective, you actually 'see' yourself moving around in an imagined future scenario, much like a camera would follow you or an external onlooker would. Research has confirmed that planning a future activity using a third-person rather than a first-person imagery produces a more accurate estimate for completion [152]. But researchers found that around two thirds of people tend to adopt a first-person perspective and this is where the problem lies. This is because people who imagine a future task from a first-person perspective are more inclined to focus on planning and less inclined to consider the obstacles in the way. As a result, they generate less realistic predictions. While people who use third-person perspective play out the scenario from an observer's point of view and are more likely to imagine potential obstacles, which leads to more realistic scenarios.

Recap

In brief, mental time travel is our only way to experience time in the past and future. We use our memories from the past to imagine the future and construct the story of our life. We visit the future every time we plan for or anticipate things to come. Anticipation creates time distortions that depend on the expected outcome. If the future events are expected to end with a loss, time will run faster, whereas time will run slowly when future events are expected to end with a gain. The experience of future time also depends on how our expectations are being met. Time will run faster when the outcome exceeds our expectations. We also saw the difference between fantasies and positive expectations and how it is important to ground those in reality to foster the kind of motivation that can bring them about.

We also looked at the planning fallacy and how it creates an optimistic bias in our future time perception. To mention a few tips to help in more accurate planning, psychologists recommend that we break down or 'unpack' a task into a number of very detailed steps needed to complete it. Whether you are getting ready for a date, finishing your holiday shopping, completing an essay, or preparing food, you will better meet your deadline by breaking it down into small steps you have to take. The greater the segmentation, the more accurate your prediction of how long the task will take. Psychologists also recommend using the third-person perspective when you are imagining your future plans. See yourself from an outside view going through the various steps you need to reach your goal. This will enable you to envision any potential hurdles and produce realistic predictions. But more importantly, consult the past. This involves predicting how long it will take to get something done based on past experiences. Remembering past experiences will lead to more realistic plans and is the secret ingredient for success. In general, adding 20 percent more time to any estimate you come up is considered wise!

It is now time to look at one of the most commonly reported distortions in how we perceive the passing of time: the experience that time seems to fly by as we grow older. Let's move on to the effects of ageing on how we experience the speed of time.

CHAPTER 12

TIME SLIPPING AWAY

The Effect of Age

'Never grow old, my little Briton. It really isn't worth the
effort'
— Richard Blake

Those were the Days

In the book Preface, I mentioned how we all remember a time in our
childhood when summer vacations appeared ridiculously long, when
weeks and months never seemed to end, and how they now seem to fly by!
Months rush by at a seemingly accelerating pace and you look back and
wonder, "Is it New Year already?" As we grow older, every year seems to
pass by more quickly than the previous one, so that the time that is left
available for us to live our lives appears to diminish with every round.

It is a fact that time seems to speed up as we age. This is true for
people from all over the world and is tremendously important because, for
many, the speeding up of time points to its ultimate end. Advances in
medical sciences have prolonged the average human life expectancy to 71

years. Statistically speaking, and depending on where you live, if you are in your 30s, you will have around 40 more years to live. This might seem like plenty of time but, at the rate at which time is speeding up, you do not want to be surprised when you reach the end and exclaim: "What?! Already?!" In order for that not to happen, we need to look at ways to slow the apparent speed of time to allow us to use the time we have left more efficiently. But first, let us explore the fundamental reasons behind this effect and, using everything we have learned so far, later explore how best to mitigate it.

Researchers have been investigating the effect of age on time perception for more than a century. Several human studies have shown that people feel the time passing faster now compared to when they were younger. In one study, researchers asked participants to tap with their hand at a 'speed which is comfortable for them' and measured the time interval between taps to determine the individual's 'internal tempo'. The 'comfortable' tapping speed is normally related to the brain's internal clock speed, so it gives an indication about the perceived speed of time. They found that elderly participants had slower tapping speeds than younger ones, which meant that their 'internal clocks' ran slower than those of younger people [153, 154, 155]. Similarly, researchers conducted an experiment with two groups of volunteers: people in their 20s and others in their 60s. The participants were asked to estimate, by silently counting, when 3 minutes of time had elapsed. The study found that the internal clock of people in their 60s seemed to be running 20% slower than it was in the young people. A slower internal clock, as we saw earlier, leads to the experience that time flew [156]. If, for instance, an elderly person was engaged in an activity that lasted one hour of real time, his internal clock, running 20% slower, would measure only 48 minutes when that one-hour activity is over. At that rate, a 24-hour day would feel like only 19 hours of experienced time. Five hours would subjectively be 'lost' from every day creating the feeling that time flew.

These experiments had the drawback of testing only short durations (seconds, minutes, and hours) and their results could not be generalized to apply to time distortions for longer periods, e.g. days, months, or years. Much larger studies were needed to address this issue. In 2005, psychologists interviewed 499 German and Austrian individuals ranging from 14 to 94 years old, asking them how quickly time seemed to pass during the previous week, month, year, and decade. They found that the biggest difference was for the 10-year interval, where older people reported that the last decade had passed more quickly than the younger group did [157]. A similar experiment was conducted in 2013, in which 868 Japanese participants, aged between 16 and 80 years old, were asked: 'how fast did the previous ten years pass for you?' They similarly found that older adults perceived time as passing quickly, compared to younger adults and, the older one is, the faster time appeared to pass. The elderly individuals also reported experiencing more time pressure compared to when they were younger, as if there was not enough time to complete all the things they wanted to do [158]. Let us now look at what causes this effect.

Routine and Living in the Past

There are several reasons, both psychological and physiological, behind why time seems to speed up as we age. As we have seen earlier, we remember the duration of an event by the amount of information and number of memories that we can recall from that event. A time interval will appear to be longer if it is rich with interesting memories. In his famous 1890 book, *The Principles of Psychology*, William James argues that 'the shortening of the years as we grow older is due to the monotony of the memory's content and the consequent simplification of the backward-glancing view'. He suggested that 'emptiness, monotony, and familiarity are what make time shrivel up'. When we were younger, everything was new so we paid more attention to the world around us. There were so many experiences to discover, interesting things to observe, and a whole world to explore. This non-stop supply of novelty meant that our young brains were constantly on high alert. A toddler's inquisitive brain, their natural curiosity, and appetite for learning come naturally. Children are known for their innocent sense of wonder and intensity of perception. Their brains are constantly bombarded with fresh new information that needs to be processed and new tasks that need to be learned, all of which requires a significant amount of brainpower to be focused on that present moment. During that phase, the child's brain is working overtime and the brain processing speed is running in high gear. Everything they see, smell, hear, or taste is new. This heightened alertness causes time to stretch in those moments. Moreover, when all of those fascinating memories are recalled, that period will appear stretched retrospectively, as if time ran slowly.

The amount of novelty continues to increase as the child grows into a teen. Between the ages of 15 and 25, there is more freedom and new experiences to explore. There are more 'firsts' and these memories are usually densely packed. There is a first love, first kiss, first alcoholic drink, first sexual relationship, and first time away from home. Psychologists refer to that period as the 'reminiscent bump'. These rich memories are easily remembered because they occur during the formative years when a person's identity is being consolidated. These novel experiences create so many memory markers that when they are recalled, that period of time will appear to have taken longer than it actually did. Time will seem to have been running slowly. This goes on until the late twenties when people start to settle down. In our thirties, our lifestyle often starts to become more organized and predictable. We may find a steady job, establish a family with the usual home chores and rhythm that repeats itself week after week. The amount of new experiences decreases and things become much more familiar. There is less novelty and we slowly lose that childish sense of wonder. We gradually stop paying conscious attention to the things around us - the town we live in, the buildings, streets, and our route to work- since we have seen those a million times. Our brain starts ignoring most of the familiar things and ceases to notice the small details that makes one day different from another. With fewer unique memories being recorded, the period of time will be experienced as being shorter. As a result, a year of childhood that is full of rich memories will seem longer than a year of adulthood which has fewer interesting memory markers. When you feel that the years are flying by, routine and monotony are the culprits. It is like when you go to sleep and wake up 8 hours later and feel the whole night was just a couple of seconds long, because your brain has stopped processing new memories. A couple of decades will feel the same way if your brain spends that time in a routine that is devoid of novel experiences.

Another factor that leads to the speeding up of time as we grow older has to do with time perspectives. Recall that time appears to slow when anticipating a positive future. Well, this can also explain why time speeds up as we age. Children live mostly in the future. Their whole lives are still ahead of them. They are eager to grow up and are constantly anticipating something good to happen, even though they will later long for their childhood. Young girls pretend to put on make-up as if they are grown-up women already. Young students are eager to graduate from high school or college, get their first car, their first job, and become independent. During those years, positive anticipation generally runs high and the awareness of time is great. This heightened attention to future approaching events causes time to slow down, as we saw in the previous chapter. That period will, therefore, inevitably appear to be stretched. In contrast, as we grow older, we slowly start to live in the past, recalling accomplishments and misfortunes from our younger years. The greater portion of our life now lies behind us and life's most important milestones, such as school graduation, first job, marriage, and having children, are no longer anticipated events but have now been transformed into past memories. With fewer things to anticipate and a relatively less optimistic future, time speeds up. President Theodore Roosevelt once said, "The only time you really live fully is from thirty to sixty. The young are slaves to dreams; the old servants of regrets. Only the middle-aged have all their five senses in the keeping of their wits."

'When you feel that the years are flying by, routine and monotony are the culprits'

Fading Memories

Another reason why time runs faster as we age is a phenomenon called 'forward telescoping'. We have all bumped into an old friend or college mate who we have not seen for years and it seems like just yesterday when we were last with them. You visit an old friend, expecting his son to be a toddler, only to find out he has been in school for a few years now and you wonder how time flew. This is called 'Forward Telescoping' and is the tendency to recall events as being more recent than they really are. It is like looking at an object through a telescope and getting the impression that it is much closer than it really is. One plausible explanation for this was proposed by Psychologist Norman Bradburn and is called the 'clarity of memory' hypothesis. As memories fade over time, they become unclear and we assume that they happened a long time ago. However, not all memories fade in the same way. Negative memories fade faster because of our psychological coping mechanism that helps us in healing wounds and moving on. In contrast, as positive memories are nice to recall, we talk about them and relive them regularly, so they are reinforced in our mind. As a result, negative memories lose their edge over time and fade faster, but positive ones persist. The clarity of these positive memories compared to the fading negative ones is what makes them appear more recent than they really are. This is the reason we remember the birth of our child, the year we graduated, or got married, as only yesterday. We often ask questions like "Is it New Year already?" or "Is it really four years since the last World Cup?" because these events were memorable and appear more recent, giving the impression that time is speeding up.

An Aging Brain

One of the unavoidable facts of life is that our brains are going to deteriorate as we grow older. This is another physiological factor behind why getting older affects our time perception. An ageing brain also goes through physical changes, such as a drop in the levels of dopamine neurotransmitters and the gradual deterioration of the central nervous system. Neurotransmitters, as we saw earlier, are the means by which brain cells communicate with each other and play a critical role in time perception [159]. When they are abundant in the brain, information processing is fast and the internal clock runs faster. However, neurotransmitters start to decline over the course of a normal lifespan causing the brain's internal clock to run slower, so time durations shrink in our mind and time appears to fly.

Likewise, as we grow older, the reduced sensitivity of our central nervous system results in a slower brain processing speed and higher memory loss. We notice that it takes us longer to solve problems or make decisions than when we were young. This is the result of wear and tear on all the axons wires which connect our brain regions together. The slow transfer of information along the axon lines impedes processing speed. This has been demonstrated in Flicker Fusion experiments which found that our ability to distinguish a fast flickering light source diminishes with age [160]. Children can distinguish flickering lights at higher frequencies than older people. This ability continues to improve with the development and maturation of their central nervous system and reaches a peak between the age of 16 and 20 years old. After that, it starts to decline, indicating a slower speed in processing information which gives the impression that time must have been running at a faster pace [161].

Squeezing Out More Time

Another reason why time feels like it is running faster as we age is due to time pressure from deadlines and the increased responsibilities that accompany adulthood. As we move away from life's beginning and start approaching life's end, we become more aware of the shrinking amount of time remaining in our life. With more commitments and loose ends to tie up, we get the feeling that there is 'so much to do and so little time'. This affects the planning and implementing of long-term goals that may not be achieved before our time runs out [162]. We become motivated to complete these goals as fast as possible, which results in a feeling that we are running out of time. William Penn, the founder of the state of Pennsylvania, described it best, "Time is what we want most, but what we use worst." Such time pressure builds up over the span of a lifetime and gets worse the older we get. As we move through life, from the optimistic prospects of ignorant youth to the more serious and restrained expectations of adulthood, we all come to a point where we have to ask ourselves one of the toughest questions, "Is that it? Is that all there is?"

When we were young, we did not care about wasting time, because we thought time was infinite. As children, we always expected things to get better when we grew up. As young adults still, the future looked promising and was filled with dreams that we wanted to have come true. But upon reaching adulthood, we started acquiring the complex roles of husband or wife and professional. Middle age is characterized by overlapping roles that create a sense of 'chronic emergency' where we feel under constant pressure to perform them in a routine fashion. A typical middle-aged woman in her 30's or 40's is a mother, a wife, and a professional, all at the same time. She has to switch constantly between these roles over the course of a typical day. We will all experience that at one point in our life. This chronic urgency creates the perception that time is running faster, as we struggle to be all things to all people. Then, all of a sudden, we realize that half of our life is over and we do not really have much to show for it. Midlife crisis kicks in and we feel that we have so much that we still want to do but not enough time to do it in. To quote from Haruki Murakami's novel *Dance, Dance, Dance*, 'Unfortunately, the clock is ticking, the hours are going by. The past increases, the future recedes. Possibilities decreasing, regrets mounting.' Our dreams take a hit with the harsh realization of the amount of time we have to spend to achieve them, compared to the diminishing time remaining.

We start having body aches, sagging skin, poor eyesight, and we realize that our time is drawing near. When that happens, most of us will not be ready. We ask ourselves, "What happened to all that money I was supposed to make, all those great times I was meant to have, and all those dreams I planned to achieve? Is that really it?" Sadly, there is probably no satisfying answer to that question. And so we react, each in his own way, to this awareness of the impending end that is creeping up on us. Some of us try to confront it by tackling the age-related symptoms. We go on a diet, join a gym, or endure plastic surgery. Anything to make us feel young again. Some others might lose themselves to alcohol, drugs, or exotic pleasures. Anything to keep their mind of that nagging question. Still, some of us will try to ignore it altogether and renew our efforts to achieve whatever can be salvaged from these unrealized dreams, trying to get some time back in a last attempt to do something with what is left. This leads to more time pressure than what was experienced in the past, reinforcing the notion that time is speeding up as we grow older [163]. It is a race against the clock and it gets worse if, as we saw earlier, we happen to be living in a fast-paced city.

Fortunately, time does not speed up forever. When we finally reach 70 or 80 years old, and this is certainly a privilege denied to many, the speed of time actually starts slowing down again. This is because we start experiencing 'role losses'. As children leave home, our parenthood role is diminished, we lose our professional role when we retire from work, and we eventually lose our role as a husband or wife with widowhood. The roles we began acquiring at the start of adulthood are lost, one-by-one, until, like in teenage years, we are back to one role only: which is what the World Health Organization defines as a 'senior citizen'. A person whose active contribution to society is no longer possible. With fewer things to do and more free time, time essentially slows down. We would have gone through a complete cycle, from childhood where time ran slow, to adulthood where it speeds up, and finally old age when it slows down again. Assuming you are in the middle of that cycle, where time is speeding up, what can you do to slow it down? That is the topic of our next and final chapter. For now, let us just summarize what we have covered here.

Recap

In brief, time appears to speed up as we grow older for a variety of reasons. Familiarity that leads to inattention is one of the chief reasons. The slower information processing speed of an ageing brain, aggravated by an increase in routine that reduces the quantity and intensity of mental snapshots, is the main culprit. Another reason is the time pressure created by the increase in responsibilities and roles that come with adulthood. All those factors produce a nagging feeling that there is not have enough time to do all the things we want to do, and that has tremendous negative implications for the way we live our life and our overall well-being.

In his book, *On the Shortness of Life*, written about 2,000 years ago, the Roman philosopher Seneca was amazed by how people were terribly busy running around, wasting their time carelessly, and belittling the time they have for living. He observed that, 'People are so prudent in protecting their personal property; but as soon as it comes to squandering time they are most wasteful of the one thing in which it is right to be stingy.' Everyone seemed to be trading their time for something, but in exchange for what? And was it worth it? Seneca's advice is 'Life is long if you know how to use it.' The message is clear. Our time on Earth is limited and uncertain and, though we may live a very healthy life, we cannot really add any real time to its span. But we can make it seem long if we know how use our time to live in a more fulfilling way. Rather than looking back at the years, wondering how they passed by so quickly, we can reverse the consequences of the age-related time-speeding effects, and truly start seeing the passing years as time that was well spent. The next chapter will bring together a lot of we have covered so far and provide some ideas on how to make next year the longest year of our life.

PART FOUR

HOW TO MAKE EVERY SECOND COUNT?

Putting it into Practice

CHAPTER 13

CRAFTING THE LONGEST YEAR OF YOUR LIFE

'The two most important days of your life are the day you
are born and the day you find out why'
— Mark Twain

'If I were to begin life again, I should want it as it was. I
would only open my eyes a little more'
— Jules Renard

'It is how we choose what we do, and how we approach it,
that will determine whether the sum of our days adds up to
a formless blur, or to something resembling a work of art'
— Mihaly Csikszentmihalyi

Living in the Moment

In this last chapter, we will look at some useful tips that we covered so far
on how to slow down time so that both the time we have already spent
living, and the time that we have left, is perceived to be long. These are not
intended as rules on how to live our lives, but examples of how adopting

just some of this thinking will help us to look back at our life and feel it was long and fulfilling. Let us start with living in the moment.

Life is a series of moments. It is not lived in daily or monthly increments, but one moment at a time. When we are planning things, we tend to use large chunks of time, such as imagining a dinner party that will last 4 hours, a three month school term, a one year lease, a two day weekend, etc. But to expand our experience of time, we should try to live with the smallest interval of time possible in mind, say one minute at a time. When we are aware that life is lived at that time scale, we will consciously make an effort to focus on the present and make the most of each moment. But how can we make ourselves more aware of these moments? A simple trick to help achieving that is to plan your calendar using odd times. You can set your alarm clock to wake you up at 6:23 a.m. instead of the usual 6:30 a.m. Your reminder to go to the gym goes off at 8:48 a.m. When you plan a meeting at work that starts at 10:30, you can put 10:26 a.m. in your calendar, so not only you make it on time and make sure the meeting actually ends on time, but you break away from the common 30 or 60 minute view.

Sometimes, the moments when we are fully alert and aware of the present occur by pure chance. It could be a car crash, a glance from a stunning woman (or man), a shooting star, a sunset or a sunrise, or the birth of a newborn baby. Whatever it is that captures our full attention, that makes our eyes open wide, and leaves us speechless. We saw previously how feelings of awe achieve the same effect of slowing down time. In those rare moments, we become fully alert and our brains start recording every bit of detail. But we do not have to wait for such events to occur by chance. Rather, we should train our minds to focus with that same alertness and intensity that allows us to control and slow down the speed of time at will. Boosting alertness does not require the drug stimulants or mind-enhancers that we saw in Chapter 9, but can be achieved with a healthy brain diet supported by a reduction in stress levels, enough sleep, and physical exercise. Those factors have been shown to be vital to a healthy alert brain that is capable of recording reality at the speed needed to slow down time.

It also helps to organize your life around your chronotype concentration curve that we saw in Chapter 8. Depending on whether you are a morning or a night person, you should engage in the important activities that matter most to you during your prime time when your alertness levels are at their peak. Maintaining a constantly alert brain would allow us to capture and process the rich details from any activity we were engaged in, with a heightened state of awareness, which would make the remembered moment seem longer. Life unfolds in the present, so we should seize that precious moment and absorb its peculiarities before it slips away unobserved.

Living in the moment is all about being fully alive 'now'. It occurs when you take a step back, meditate on some deep thoughts, take a deep breath, and smell some roses. Have you ever been to a forest at night? Have you ever had a chance to listen to its enchanting sounds? Maybe it was at a camping trip with some friends? Or on a visit to your grandpa's house up in the mountains? When I was in cub scouts, we used to go camping in forests near rivers or lakes. When it got late at night, we would gather around a bonfire to roast marshmallows and tell creepy stories. We would play a game that consisted of keeping extremely quiet just to listen and identify every forest sound that we could possibly hear. A cracking fire, a chirp, a few sudden wolf howls or owl screeches, the constant sound of rustling leaves in the wind, or a gentle stream trickling nearby. You would be amazed at what goes on in the background that gets ignored by our brain, because they are deemed uninteresting. During those few minutes of playing that game, time almost came to a halt. Those fascinating moments stretched and became truly unforgettable, largely because they were spent fully alert to that present moment that allowed rich memories to be recorded. In the same way, our brain can absorb many more memories that otherwise would have gone unnoticed by simply focusing on the present. To slow down time, it is therefore important to be mindful and focused on the present moment in everything we do.

When on vacation, paying attention to all those tiny details unfolding around us, whether eating a delicious cake, enjoying the scenery, basking in the warm sunshine, or just feeling a gentle breeze, will create memorable moments that will stretch that time in our mind. Stop to look at that weird cloud in the sky or at that beautiful sunset. If you are having a meal, rather than reading the newspaper or checking the latest on social media, concentrate on the taste of the food. Savor your meal, at least the first 3 bites. Just soak in as much of today as you possibly can – the sights, sounds, smells, and emotions, and when you look back at the time spent, it will feel much longer.

We live in the moment when we stop living in the past, enjoy the present, and look forward to the future. Novelist Paulo Coelho notes, "We think so much about the future that we neglect the present, and thus experience neither the present nor the future." Our brain's default mode of operation is future thinking and so we all worry about things that might happen and anticipate future events. But most worries are exaggerated scenarios that never happen. When we are at work, we dream about being on vacation and when on vacation, we worry about all the work that is stacking up for our return. We also tend to dwell on the intrusive memories of the past and things we should have done or not done, or things we should have said or not said. Past and future thinking is an immense and useless drain to our energy and time.

By living in the present moment instead, we can channel all our energy on what we are doing now or on whom we are with. Living the perfect moment and experiencing the state of 'flow' that we covered in Chapter 5 can only happen when we are mindful and fully immersed in what we are doing to the extent that we become totally oblivious to the passage of time. By being 'in the zone,' the experienced durations will feel short, but the remembered durations will feel long because of all the collected memories and that is extremely gratifying. Moreover, when experienced durations shrink, we will judge that as being pleasant (remember the reverse relation between time and having fun). Consequently, the remembered durations will stretch with those rich mental snapshots, which in turn stretches the view of our past.

'We live in the moment when we stop living in the past, enjoy the present, and look forward to the future'

Live Long and Prosper

We all want to live a long and happy life. Longevity and happiness are two aspects of our being that we all strive to achieve. An important factor contributing to our happiness is the feeling that we have lived a long life and the feeling that we still have enough time in our life to fulfill all of our dreams. Psychologists describe happiness as ranging from simple contentment to intense joy. It is such an essential emotion to all humans that the United States Declaration of Independence considers "life, liberty and the pursuit of happiness" to be unalienable rights. We all tend to evaluate the quality of our life primarily by how happy we are. But what makes us happy has been the subject of many theories. The 'Comparison Theory' claims that we judge the quality of our lives by estimating the gap between the reality we are living in and what we think is the 'common standard of good'. In this view, happiness largely involves keeping up with the Jones. The 'Need Theory' on the other hand states that happiness is an inner reflection of how we feel and is an indicator of whether certain needs are satisfied. In this view, experiences will add to our happiness only if they gratify some need or desire. Closely related to that is the fact that we all tend to have a vague idea of what we would like to accomplish before we die. If we come close to attaining that goal or partly achieve it, we become happy. If it remains beyond our reach, we grow bitter. Finally, the 'Set-Point Theory' maintains that our level of happiness is a somewhat constant personality trait and that whatever we do, we cannot change our happiness levels by much. Some people are naturally just happier than others. Accordingly, happy experiences can only offer a brief mood uplift, which eventually fades away as we return to our inherent happiness set-point. This is evident, for instance, from the fact that the positive effects of a holiday do not last very long, and people normally return to their pre-vacation happiness levels within 2 to 3 weeks. But what defines this happiness set-point? Is it something genetic that we are naturally born with or can it modified?

In an interesting study, neuroscientist Dr. Richard Davidson at the University of Wisconsin found that people were more happy and energetic when the left part of their brain was highly active, and were more depressed and in an anxious mood when the right part of their brain was more active. This is supported by evidence that extroverts are generally happier than introverts and the left part of their brain has been shown to be more active than their right part. The ratio of left-to-right activity therefore indicates the happiness set-point level that people tended to always return to, regardless of whether they had just won the lottery or lost a loved one. Using an fMRI machine, Dr. Davidson scanned the brains of Buddhist monks, some of which had spent many years of their lives in meditation. The results of the brain imaging studies showed that, during meditation, the left part of the monks brains became highly active and tended to overrule the right part, thus raising the happiness set-point levels. Further studies with normal participants, indicated that eight weeks of a one-hour daily mindfulness practice can significantly increase the left-side brain activity and happiness levels, for up to four months from when the training program ended. As we already saw in Chapter 4, mindfulness is a meditation technique that helps people live in the moment and be aware of the present as it is unfolding now. This enhanced focus on the present, slows down time subjectively and creates the feeling that there is ample time to achieve the things we want to do. That positive outlook is what boosts people's happiness levels, as Dr. Davidson discovered.

Mindfulness is easy to learn even for people who have never practiced meditation. In one study, people who were trained to do it for just 20 minutes a day and for just five days, showed a significant improvement in concentration skills and had lower anxiety and stress symptoms [164]. Studies have also shown that mindfulness reduces stress, boosts the immune system, lowers blood pressure, and reduces the risk of heart disease. Mindfulness meditation can also teach us the kind of focus and concentration that slows the pace of time and brings more intensity to our experiences, thus making them more memorable. By practicing mindfulness meditation, we enhance our ability to live in the moment, which is critical for collecting the necessary mental snapshots that our mind will later use to recreate the perceived span of our life. With enough practice, mindfulness can become a permanent mental state, that has been described as a state of "presence of mind" where we are clearly aware of our inner and outer world, including our thoughts, sensations, and emotions as they occur at any given moment. By being mindful of the present, we will not allow life to pass by without living it. Moreover, by slowing things down, we will perceive time as more abundant and will be able to do all the things we wanted to do. Therefore, by focusing on the present moment through mindfulness, time slows down and, in turn, our overall happiness levels surge [165].

Collecting Memorable Moments

In addition to the aspiration for a happy life, we all wish to live a long one. A healthy lifestyle is necessary for prolonging the total number of years we live, but that is not sufficient enough to increase our perceived life span. A man who dies at the age of 40 might have subjectively lived a longer and more fulfilling life than a man who dies at the age of 90, if he has lived a life that is rich with memories of sensational experiences. Worse still for the man of 90 would be reaching a point in his life when, for whatever reason, he simply stops living, in the true sense of the word. "Some people die at 25 and aren't buried until 75", said Benjamin Franklin, one of the founders of the United States. In that sense, the meaning of life is life itself. Life is for living and you are truly alive when you are living your dreams. 'Start living or get busy dying' is a great advice from the Oscar-winning movie *Shawshank Redemption*.

When we look back at our life from our present moment, we become aware of its span, starting from our earliest childhood consciousness, right through to all of those experiences that make us 'us'. We have seen, in part three of the book that we perceive the length of our life in terms of the number of memories we have accumulated. But as we grow older, the amount of routine in our daily lives increases, the speed of time accelerates, and the remaining years get shorter and shorter. When we were children, life stretched before us as though it will never end. But, upon reaching adulthood, it starts rushing by and we feel like there is not enough time left to realize all of our hopes and dreams. When this is combined with fading memories, our life span starts to shrink in our mind and we reach a point when we ask that dreadful question: "Is that all there is?"

The answer to perceived longevity lies in our ability to collect pleasant memories. As we saw in Chapter 10, to improve our perception and perceived duration of the past we will have to increase the number of memories we capture and retain in our minds. There are a few things we can do to help us achieve that. As a start, the greater the variety of experiences we have and the more vivid the memory of them, the longer our life will seem. A varied, diverse, and fulfilled life is also a long one. Our brains love novelty. If your brain is exposed to a great deal of new information over the course of a day, and the following day receives hardly any new information, the first day will seem much longer than the second. An action packed weekend filled with interesting new activities compared to a weekend that you spent sick with flu at home doing nothing, will be perceived longer in duration when you recollect it. You might have been away for only two days, but it feels that you have been gone forever. That adventure weekend will last longer in your mind and become part of your life story whereas the time when you were sick will quickly be forgotten, as if it was never a part of your life. You do not have to participate in extreme sports such as skydiving, rock climbing or surf boarding to create excitement and novelty. You could simply take a salsa class or take a new route to work. Therefore, the key to slow down time is to avoid routine tasks as much as possible and introduce novelty and diversity in your activities.

'A varied, diverse, and fulfilled life is also a long one'

As we age, we become accustomed to the familiar environments we live in. So visiting new places can offer ample new experiences and memories for the brain to process. You do not have to travel far to explore novelty. This can be just around the corner, perhaps a new restaurant or coffee shop that you have never tried before. Rather than sticking to the usual familiar places, try something new. New sounds, people, tastes, colors, textures, and smells sends massive information to your brain and provide lasting memories which, when recalled, will cause time to stretch. Essentially, constantly seek out new experiences in order to slow down the speed at which life is running.

'The answer to perceived longevity lies in our ability to collect pleasant memories'

Meeting new people also provides the brain with a lot of information to chew on such as their characters, accents, voices, facial expressions, and body language. Having meaningful and interesting social interactions will therefore create rich long-term memories and longer recalled durations. Joining a social club, a book club, or perhaps a hobby group where you can constantly meet new people will help in slowing down time. Spending time with people you love also slows down time. This is even more important, since relationships form the pillar of a purposeful life.

Another way to increase the number of memories is to supply your brain with new information so that it is constantly learning new things. This could be a new language, a new course, or a new skill. In fact, researchers at Penn State University found that learning a second language changes the brain's network, making it more flexible and efficient, in what could be the brain's best workout [166]. It is also never too late to start the things we always wanted to do but never found the time to. Learn to play a musical instrument, read a do-it-yourself book, or start a new hobby. Keep challenging yourself and raise the bar with progressively higher goals. Surround yourself with inspiring people. It could be an intellectual friend, a kind-hearted pal, or perhaps your old friend from high school! Indulge in intellectual and cultural events, or maybe write a book! The key is to keep your brain active by regularly supplying it with fresh information! Essentially, become a student again and do not ever stop learning. This will boost the number of memory markers you collect every day and slow down time.

Some people have it in their character to enjoy learning, absorb new information, and experience the world to the fullest. For those, time would go slow and life is long and rich. Other people who do not bother to learn anything new, are not inquisitive, and are content to go with just the bare minimum, will experience time speeding up. Imagine being invited to spend a few days on the most wondrous and exciting island, splendid in beauty, and magical in every way. An inquisitive mind would soak in every sensation, they would learn about the tiniest details, get immersed in every experience, and be constantly alert to capture every mental snapshot from that exhilarating place. As a result, their experience of the time spent there would stretch. A disinterested person, on the other hand, would not care to learn or absorb anything going on around them. Their primary concern would be merely eating, drinking and sleeping. Their recollection of the few days spent on that island will barely make an impression in their mind and will shrink into practically nothing. Well, you do not have to wait for such a special invitation, you are already there. There is no island that is more wondrous and exciting than this beautiful lovely planet we live on. As Jules Renard would say, 'On earth there is no heaven, but there are pieces of it everywhere.' We have all been given an exclusive VIP invitation, a privilege denied to many, to spend a limited amount of time there and must decide how to make best use of it. The world is full of sensations waiting to be become memorable reminiscences, marvelous encounters waiting to be experienced, and spectacular wonders waiting to be observed. The great Lebanese poet Kahlil Gibran says it well, "Forget not that the earth delights to feel your bare feet, and the winds long to play with your hair." So do not wait until it is too late; the purpose of life is to live it to the fullest. We just need to be alert, intent to observe, willing to inquire, and open to learn, so that we may enjoy it and stretch it as long as possible.

Improving Our Attention and Memory

To be able to focus on living in the moment and collect memorable mental snapshots, it also helps to improve the capacity of our short-term memory and attention span. As we grow older, it is quite normal to forget things. We forget what we had for breakfast or where we put our keys. Sometimes you walk into a room and forget why. You meet a new colleague at work then immediately forget her name. This is a sign of ageing, and it is the biggest cause of short-term memory loss. Our brains stop growing and actually start shrinking from the age of 20 onwards. However, there are several ways to improve short-term memory and prevent that deterioration from seriously affecting our time experience. Several self-help books are available on brain training and learning memory techniques. I recommend *Moonwalking with Einstein: The Art and Science of Remembering Everything* by Joshua Foer or any of Tony Buzan books. Studies have found that dementia is delayed in elderly people who do crosswords, puzzles, read, and play card games. Online apps and memory improvement games that come with a daily dose of memory training are also quite helpful. I recommend *Luminosity* or *Fit Brains*, which are free online brain training apps that offer a wide range of scientifically proven memory games for all ages. In addition, consuming a healthy brain diet or taking memory supplements is another way to keep a vigorous memory.

Building Anticipation

Anticipation of a positive event slows down time, as we saw already in chapter 11, and introducing anticipation into our lives helps in slowing it down. When we have to wait for something to happen, time feels like it runs more slowly. In most cases, this might be annoying, but we can use that to our advantage. For instance, you could build anticipation and excitement when planning a date or organizing a long summer vacation. That anticipation will increase your alertness level and direct your attention to the passing time causing it to slow down, in a pleasant and exciting way. Anticipation also increases the intensity of our emotions. Most people, for instance, experience deep emotional reactions when anticipating their Thanksgiving holiday then when they later recall it [167]. Anticipation is more intense than retrospection. This is because future events are less certain than past events and uncertainty amplifies emotions. As we saw previously, more intense emotions slow the speed of time.

We also saw that when we recall a vacation we had in the past, it will only seem long if it contained lots of interesting memories. But research has shown that, anticipating a future vacation will also slow down the time leading to it. Moreover, it seems that people derive more pleasure planning their vacation than later recalling it. The reason is future uncertainty. Your highly anticipated beach holiday might turn out different in many ways compared to the one way it ended up happening. There are many more beaches you might visit, many more restaurants you might eat in, many more places you might see, and many more people you might meet, than the actual beach, restaurant, sites, and people you ended up seeing. This uncertainty makes an anticipated vacation more exciting and amplifies the pleasant rewards in your mind.

Research on how people enjoy their vacation have concluded that anticipating and planning a vacation is even more enjoyable than the vacation itself. It is like Winnie-the-Pooh describing his love for honey, "Well, although Eating Honey was a very good thing to do, there was a moment just before you began to eat it which was better than when you were". But Winnie did not know what that moment was called. It is a moment of eager anticipation that heightens mental arousal and slows time. People look forward to their vacations and, for most, the enjoyment starts weeks, even months, before the vacation actually starts. That is what researchers from the Netherlands found when they surveyed 1,530 Dutch vacationers and measured their happiness levels before and after they took their vacation [168]. The largest boost in happiness came from the simple act of planning the vacation. Anticipation boosted happiness for about 8 weeks prior to the vacation. After the vacation, happiness quickly dropped back to baseline levels in a matter of just 2 to 3 weeks, regardless of how long the vacation lasted. In brief, expecting a good thing is sometimes more enjoyable than actually experiencing it [169]. Therefore, you can get more fun out of several small vacations in a year than from one big one. Two one-week long holidays are probably better than one two-week holiday, and that is probably better than a long one-month long holiday, because they create more excitement and things to look forward to during the year.

But you do not have to plan everything to the last detail to create more anticipation. Just having a rough itinerary before the trip is enough to increase excitement. The level of planning has to also be balanced against how much you leave for chance. It is beneficial to introduce some spontaneity to a certain extent, instead of planning every move. Any unexpected surprises make us more alert and the vacation becomes excitingly more adventurous, as we look forward in anticipation to what will happen next. A friend of mine experienced the longest vacation of his life when he took a two-week trip with his girlfriend on a 5,000 km tour on bike in India. Without any prior hotel bookings and an erratic weather, the adventure boosted their alertness and created so much anticipation that slowed down time and made it more memorable.

The more you spend time planning, talking about, and anticipating an event, while keeping a certain level of spontaneity, the more enjoyable it will be and the slower time flows. This principle can be applied to any area of your life. Therefore, always have something to anticipate, something nice to wake up to in the morning, or an exciting thing to do after work. It could be seeing a person, doing a hobby, or simply just eating great food. Anything that excites you and spur your creativity will make you happier and having constant anticipation in your life will slow it down.

Time is not Money

As we already saw, time is actually more precious than money because it is our most scarce resource. It is absurd how we are willing to spend our time to earn more money, but reluctant to spend money in stretching and slowing down time. We spend our precious time in making money, but that is worthless if it is not spent on creating exciting memories that can stretch out our remembered past and make life more fulfilling. In a sense, money can create more subjective time when it is spent on enjoying life and generating the memory-making ingredients that are necessary for expanding our retrospective perception of life.

We saw in the book Introduction that a Gallup survey of 450,000 Americans, concluded that when people's annual income passed above 75,000 U.S dollars, they became more satisfied but not happier. There is a limit to how much more can money make us happy. The survey concluded that earning more than that income threshold does not contribute further to our emotional well-being [2]. It follows logically that any time spent on making more than 75,000 U.S dollars a year is, in a sense, wasted time as it does not make us happier. Additionally, if we think of time in terms of money, rather than spending our time on interesting experiences, we will end up working longer hours to make more money. Relaxing at the pool becomes a waste of time. Having dinner with the family becomes a luxury that is hard to justify. Even when we manage to take some time off, it will be rushed by the worry that we could be working more. The result is we stop enjoying life and miss it entirely as it swiftly slips by.

Moreover, recent research has confirmed that, paradoxically, the more you work, the less you get done. Bringing home more work, or constantly checking your email in the evening or over the weekend does not help. An interesting rule called Parkinson's Law states that your workload will expand to whatever time you allocate for its completion. The proof is in what psychologists refer to as the Vacation Paradox (different from the Holiday Paradox) which states that: you may never be able to finish all your work on a regular day, but a couple days before you go on vacation, you somehow manage to complete everything planned on that day in addition to that backlog of work that has been stacking on your desk. This is only possible because when you have an endpoint to your workday, you will work more efficiently and get things done. By having a specific end to your workday or workweek, where you can disconnect and take your mind off work, you will be able to do all the other things you have always wanted to do but never had the time for. Having an end to work will not only help you to work more efficiently, but life will slow down and you will live a more balanced and fulfilling life.

Researchers have also confirmed that people who are constantly 'connected' to technology are generally more anxious and perceive time as flowing faster than usual. In this day and age, emails and social media have become an integral part of our lives. Whether it is Facebook, Twitter, WhatsApp, Instagram, or Snapchat, etc., we constantly check these sites for updates on the latest happenings around us and that can become addictive. This steals precious time away from other more meaningful things that actually make us happy. It is far better to check emails only twice a day. Choose one or two social media channels and check them once or twice a day at most. The time you save can be used to start a new hobby. In his 1962 book, *Of Time, Work and Leisure*, Pulitzer Prize–winning author and political scientist Sebastian de Grazia gives a great advice, 'Lean back under a tree, put your arms behind your head, wonder at the pass we've come to, smile and remember that the beginnings and ends of man's every great enterprise are untidy.' Recall that old Buddhist wisdom:

'Act always as if the future of the universe depended on what you did, while laughing at yourself for thinking that whatever you do makes any difference'

Resisting Time Pressure

Are you a 'rushaholic'? Do you happen to live in one of those fast-paced cities that we covered in the Introduction, where you feel in perpetual hurry? A recent poll of over 1,000 Americans found that nearly half felt they lacked enough time in daily life. "Time famine"-the feeling of having too much to do and not enough time to do it- is the cause of unnecessary stress and reduced performance. We all tend to rush when we have so many things to do. So we start multi-tasking and that negatively affects our performance. Doing things quickly actually ends up slowing you down such as when you rush out of your house only to realize you forgot your key, phone, or wallet on the kitchen table. Assuming that by doing things faster you will get more done is a trap. Driving faster will not get you to your destination any sooner (unless you really intended to visit the hospital). Rushing things also affects the quality of your experiences. Ever finished eating a meal without tasting any of it? Rushing will not give you more time, but will sap the pleasure and value from the time that you already have. It actually speeds up time and makes it worse.

If you try to recall the evening when you were preparing dinner while helping your kids with homework and chatting with your friend, you will not remember too many details and that evening will seem short. If you jump from one project to another, you will not be dedicating enough attention to each task and, as a result, you will not perform it properly. With less devoted attention, the internal clock counter starts missing ticks, and time flies. Therefore, do not rush whatever you are doing. Resist deadline pressure, stay calm, breathe slowly, and focus on one thing at a time.

At work, if you constantly multi-task during the week, you might be able to complete small jobs but the big ones will remain open and your work pressure will increase. It is far better to seek help or delegate some of your responsibilities to reduce your workload instead of trying to do everything by yourself. It helps also to take a step back and make an honest assessment of the really important things that needs to be done. Pick three things to accomplish each day. Stop taking more commitments and learn to say no. You will feel better when you are not under pressure to do all things in the shortest time possible. By simply choosing the things that really matter to you, the things you are passionate about, and dropping the rest, you will focus better and life will less stressful as time slows down. A slower and simpler life is a happier life.

Feeling constantly harried is not a pleasant way to live. It also helps to be proactive and stay one step ahead. Being reactive only adds more worries, stress, and last minute workloads. Your attention will be diluted and your brain will be unable to record any significant memories, so that week will fly very quickly in retrospect. It would be better to concentrate on finishing one task and doing it to completion before moving onto the next one. This is true of everyday tasks, such as finishing one book before starting to read another, and of bigger life goals, like writing a best-seller book, composing the next hit song, winning an Olympic gold medal, or simply swimming with the dolphins! When this philosophy is applied to various areas in your life, you will relax and start to focus more on 'now', which will cause life to slow down. Therefore, stop multi-tasking, plan your priorities, try to complete them one at a time, and above all, take your sweet time about it!

'A slower and simpler life is a happier life.'

Inducing Feelings of Awe

One last thing to consider for slowing down time, is the need to change our perspective and, rather than getting bogged down, taking a step back and looking at the bigger picture. It helps to actually believe that time is more abundant than it seems. Inducing feelings of awe, as we saw earlier, will help in expanding time and our view on things. It does not have to involve religious or mystical experiences. Stunning natural landscapes or amazing works of art and music can open up our mind and produce the same effect. Such mind-expanding experiences will create the feeling that we have more time to accomplish the tasks we are doing. With that mindset, we will be able to relax in the present, live mindfully, and have enough time to achieve what we want. This is even more important if we actually use that extra time to contribute, even in a tiny way, to making the world a better place. In fact, several studies have observed that what goes through the minds of people on their death beds is not fast cars or more money, but their lasting impact on this world. Is the world a better place because you were here or not? We each have a unique gift to contribute, and those who contribute most, die with a smile on their face.

Conclusion

With all the tips that we covered so far, I hope you will get some ideas of how to slow the flow of time in your life and counter the effects of growing old on the shrinking years. And remember that, even if you feel that so many years have already been lost, it is actually never too late to make the most of what is left, even in old age. Every day starts as the first day of the rest of our life, so we can still make the most of it. I recall a scene from the movie *The Curious Case of Benjamin Button* where Brad Pitt, taking the role of a man ageing backwards, tells Cate Blanchett how it is never too late to be whoever we want to be, experience things that we never felt before, live a life we are proud of and if we have not done all that already, we should have the courage to start all over again. In order to feel proud of having lived a 'long' and fulfilling life, we should constantly aim to fill our infinitely precious time with vibrant and intriguing experiences to make every second count, at every point in your life, even to the last one. No one said it better than the Welsh poet Dylan Thomas, 'Do not go gently into that good night. Rage, rage against the dying of the light.'

And when your time is up, and you look back at the life you have lived, instead of feeling that you were 20 years old just yesterday, and wonder how the following decades have passed in the blink of an eye, you can instead run the film of your endless precious memories in your mind, starting with your sensational adventures, the exciting places you visited, to the interesting people you met, and all that knowledge you acquired along the way. You can then feel proud that you did your best to supply your brain with a colorful mosaic of rich memories that is worthy of an award-winning life movie! At that moment, instead of seeing your life flash before your eyes in a split of a second, you will be satisfied to watch it serenely unfold and take pleasure in the gratifying feeling of having been able to fit several lifetimes into a single one.

THE END

Author's Note

Thank you for reading The Power of Time Perception.

If you loved the book and have a minute to spare, I would really appreciate a short review on the online retailer where you bought the book. A couple of lines are enough.

Your help in spreading the word is greatly appreciated. Reviews from readers like you make a huge difference in helping new readers find my book.

*Link to my Amazon page:
https://www.amazon.com/product-reviews/0995734771/

As supplementary content, you can get **FREE** access to the **Speed of Time Online Test** that will measure how fast time runs in your mind, on the link below
http://www.subscribepage.com/speed-of-time-test

You can also download a **FREE** copy of the **Ultimate Guide to a Healthy Brain Diet** that will help you maintain an alert brain for slowing the speed of time. Please visit the author's website at http://www.jpzogby.com

Or Click here to download a **Free** copy of the Ultimate Guide to a Healthy Brain Diet

Thank you!
Jean Paul

P.S. If you'd like to know when my next book comes out or want to receive additional content on time perception, please sign up for my newsletter here –> http://www.jpzogby.com

WITHOUT WHOM

Jean Paul knows he wouldn't get a fraction of the things he wants to do if it wasn't for his awesome family and friends. A special thanks to Roula, Stephanie, Chloe, Anthony, the best family ever, for their endless love, support, and patience.

I would also like to thank all the friends who shared their own experiences of time distortions. Some were related to how time speeds up with age, others were about how time stretches on vacations or in car crashes, and a few who even shared their experience with marijuana and its effect on time!

I owe a great deal of gratitude to my Editors, Katy Hamilton and Sarah Busby, for their valuable critique and role in shaping the final book. "Kate your sharp eye to detail was instrumental" and "Sarah, I admire the way you challenge my logic. Your feedback was invaluable".

I also thank Dalchand Sharma for designing a stunning and awesome book cover. Thank you for bearing with me in all those endless changes I kept requesting.

Without the psychologists, neuroscientists, and various academics who spent years performing studies and conducting experiments, this book would not have been possible. I would like to thank the following people whose research has shaped my ideas and understanding of time perception: Paul Fraisse, Ernst Poppel, John M. Stroud, Marc Wittmann, John Wearden, David Eagleman, Lera Boroditsky, William Friendman, Philip Zombardo, Sylvie Droit-Volet, Virginei van Wassenhove, Rufin VanRullen, Mihály Csikszentmihalyi, Dan Zakay, Robert Ornstein, and Paul Mangan.

INDEX

REFERENCES

1. Dawkins, R. *The Greatest Show on Earth: The Evidence for Evolution.* (Free Press, 2010).
2. Kahneman, D. & Deaton, A. High income improves evaluation of life but not emotional well-being. *Proc. Natl. Acad. Sci. U. S. A.* **107**, 16489–93 (2010).
3. Levine, R. V., Lynch, K., Miyake, K. & Lucia, M. The Type A city: Coronary heart disease and the pace of life. *J. Behav. Med.* **12**, 509–524 (1989).
4. Levine, R. V. & Norenzayan, A. The Pace of Life in 31 Countries. *Journal of Cross-Cultural Psychology* **30**, 178–205 (1999).
5. Wittmann, M. Moments in time. *Front. Integr. Neurosci.* **5**, 66 (2011).
6. Lloyd, D. Neural correlates of temporality: default mode variability and temporal awareness. *Conscious. Cogn.* **21**, 695–703 (2012).
7. Pöppel, E. Pre-semantically defined temporal windows for cognitive processing. *Philos. Trans. R. Soc. Lond. B. Biol. Sci.* **364**, 1887–96 (2009).
8. Fraisse, P. Perception and estimation of time. *Annu. Rev. Psychol.* **35**, 1–36 (1984).
9. Pöppel, E. Lost in time: A historical frame, elementary processing units and the 3-second window. in *Acta Neurobiologiae Experimentalis* **64**, 295–301 (2004).
10. Nagy, E. Sharing the moment: the duration of embraces in humans. *J. Ethol.* **29**, 389–393 (2011).
11. Saj, a., Fuhrman, O., Vuilleumier, P. & Boroditsky, L. Patients With Left Spatial Neglect Also Neglect the 'Left Side' of Time. *Psychol. Sci.* **25**, 207–214 (2013).
12. Boroditsky, L. Does language shape thought? Mandarin and English speakers' conceptions of time. *Cogn. Psychol.* **43**, 1–22 (2001).
13. Stetson, C., Cui, X., Montague, P. R. & Eagleman, D. M. Motor-Sensory Recalibration Leads to an Illusory Reversal of Action and Sensation. *Neuron* **51**, 651–659 (2006).
14. Surwillo, W. W. The relation of decision time to brain wave frequency and to age. *Electroencephalogr. Clin. Neurophysiol.* **16**, 510–514 (1964).
15. Callaway, E. & Yeager, C. L. Relationship between reaction time and electroencephalographic alpha phase. *Science* **132**, 1765–6

(1960).

16.   Hume, D. *The Philosophical Works of David Hume, vol. 1 (Treatise of Human Nature Part 1) - Online Library of Liberty.* (1828). at <http://oll.libertyfund.org/titles/1481>

17.   VanRullen, R. & Koch, C. Is perception discrete or continuous? *Trends Cogn. Sci.* **7**, 207–213 (2003).

18.   Von Baer, K. E. Welche Auffasung der lebendigen Natur ist die richtige? *Aus Balt. Geiste- sarbeit. Reden und Aufsätze* **1**, (1908).

19.   Hylan, J. P. The distribution of attention - I. *Philos. Rev.* **13**, (1904).

20.   Stroud, J. M. The fine structure of psychological time. *Ann. N. Y. Acad. Sci.* **138**, 623–631 (1967).

21.   Johansson, A. & Sandström, M. *Sensitivity of the human visual system to amplitude modulated light.* (Arbetslivsinstitutet, 2003).

22.   Healy, K., McNally, L., Ruxton, G. D., Cooper, N. & Jackson, A. L. Metabolic rate and body size are linked with perception of temporal information. *Anim. Behav.* **86**, 685–696 (2013).

23.   Busch, N. A., Dubois, J. & VanRullen, R. The phase of ongoing EEG oscillations predicts visual perception. *J. Neurosci.* **29**, 7869–76 (2009).

24.   Mathewson, K. E., Gratton, G., Fabiani, M., Beck, D. M. & Ro, T. To see or not to see: prestimulus alpha phase predicts visual awareness. *J. Neurosci.* **29**, 2725–32 (2009).

25.   Shevelev, I. A. *et al.* Visual illusions and travelling alpha waves produced by flicker at alpha frequency. *Int. J. Psychophysiol.* **39**, 9–20 (2000).

26.   Purves, D., Paydarfar, J. a & Andrews, T. J. The wagon wheel illusion in movies and reality. *Proc. Natl. Acad. Sci. U. S. A.* **93**, 3693–3697 (1996).

27.   Kline, K., Holcombe, A. O. & Eagleman, D. M. Illusory motion reversal is caused by rivalry, not by perceptual snapshots of the visual field. *Vision Res.* **44**, 2653–2658 (2004).

28.   VanRullen, R., Reddy, L. & Koch, C. The continuous wagon wheel illusion is associated with changes in electroencephalogram power at approximately 13 Hz. *J. Neurosci.* **26**, 502–7 (2006).

29.   Simpson, W. A., Shahani, U. & Manahilov, V. Illusory percepts of moving patterns due to discrete temporal sampling. *Neurosci. Lett.* **375**, 23–7 (2005).

30.   VanRullen, R., Reddy, L. & Koch, C. Attention-driven discrete sampling of motion perception. *Proc. Natl. Acad. Sci.* **102**, 5291–5296 (2005).

31.   Buschman, T. J. & Miller, E. K. Shifting the spotlight of attention: evidence for discrete computations in cognition. *Front. Hum.*

Neurosci. **4,** 194 (2010).

32.   Chakravarthi, R. & VanRullen, R. Conscious updating is a rhythmic process. *Proc. Natl. Acad. Sci.* **109,** 10599–10604 (2012).

33.   VanRullen, R., Carlson, T. & Cavanagh, P. The blinking spotlight of attention. *Proc. Natl. Acad. Sci. U. S. A.* **104,** 19204–9 (2007).

34.   Wearden, J. H. & Penton-Voak, I. S. Feeling the heat: body temperature and the rate of subjective time, revisited. *Q. J. Exp. Psychol. B.* **48,** 129–141 (1995).

35.   College, A., Cahoon, D. & Edmonds, E. M. The watched pot still won't boil: Expectancy as a variable in estimating the passage of time. **16,** 115–116 (1980).

36.   Ozawa, R., Fujii, K. & Kouzaki, M. The return trip is felt shorter only postdictively: A psychophysiological study of the return trip effect [corrected]. *PLoS One* **10,** e0127779 (2015).

37.   Kramer, R. S. S., Weger, U. W. & Sharma, D. The effect of mindfulness meditation on time perception. *Conscious. Cogn.* **22,** 846–852 (2013).

38.   Kramer, R. S. S., Weger, U. W. & Sharma, D. The effect of mindfulness meditation on time perception. *Conscious. Cogn.* **22,** 846–52 (2013).

39.   Diaz, F. M. Mindfulness, attention, and flow during music listening: An empirical investigation. *Psychol. Music* **41,** 42–58 (2011).

40.   Sackett, A. M., Meyvis, T., Nelson, L. D., Converse, B. A. & Sackett, A. L. You're Having Fun When Time Flies: The Hedonic Consequences of Subjective Time Progression. *Psychol. Sci.* **21,** 111–117 (2010).

41.   Gerald Donaldson: Ayrton Senna at Monaco (1988). at <http://www.f1speedwriter.com/2012/05/ayrton-senna-at-monaco-1988.html>

42.   Nordin, I. A. *et al.* Attention, time perception and immersion in games. *CHI '13 Ext. Abstr. Hum. Factors Comput. Syst. - CHI EA '13* 1089 (2013). doi:10.1145/2468356.2468551

43.   Gable, P. a & Poole, B. D. Time flies when you're having approach-motivated fun: effects of motivational intensity on time perception. *Psychol. Sci.* **23,** 879–86 (2012).

44.   Csikszentmihalyi, M. *Finding Flow: The Psychology of Engagement with Everyday Life.* (BasicBooks, 1997). at <https://books.google.com/books?id=HBod-fUzmBcC&pgis=1>

45.   Del Percio, C. *et al.* 'Neural efficiency' of athletes' brain for upright standing: a high-resolution EEG study. *Brain Res. Bull.* **79,** 193–200 (2009).

46.   Minkwitz, J. *et al.* Time perception at different EEG-vigilance

levels. *Behav. Brain Funct.* **8,** 50 (2012).

47.   Cahoon, R. L. Physiological arousal and time estimation. *Percept. Mot. Skills* **28,** 259–68 (1969).

48.   Bowers, K. S. & Brenneman, H. A. Hypnosis and the perception of time. *Int. J. Clin. Exp. Hypn.* **27,** 29–41 (1979).

49.   Tse, P. U., Intriligator, J., Rivest, J. & Cavanagh, P. Attention and the subjective expansion of time. *Percept. Psychophys.* **66,** 1171–1189 (2004).

50.   Frederickx, S. *et al.* The Relationship Between Arousal and the Remembered Duration of Positive Events. *Appl. Cogn. Psychol.* **27,** 493–496 (2013).

51.   Weber, E., Patry J.L., Spychiger, M. Musik macht Schule. *Die blaue Eule* (1993).

52.   Sutoo, D. & Akiyama, K. Music improves dopaminergic neurotransmission: demonstration based on the effect of music on blood pressure regulation. *Brain Res.* **1016,** 255–62 (2004).

53.   Sridharan, D., Levitin, D. J., Chafe, C. H., Berger, J. & Menon, V. Neural dynamics of event segmentation in music: converging evidence for dissociable ventral and dorsal networks. *Neuron* **55,** 521–32 (2007).

54.   Penton-Voak, I. S., Edwards, H., Percival, A. & Wearden, J. H. Speeding up an internal clock in humans? Effects of click trains on subjective duration. *J. Exp. Psychol. Anim. Behav. Process.* **22,** 307–320 (1996).

55.   Kellaris, J. J. & Kent, R. J. The influence of music on consumers' temporal perceptions: Does time fly when you're having fun? *J. Consum. Psychol.* **1,** 365–376 (1992).

56.   Kellaris, J. J. & Altsech, M. B. The Experience of Time As a Function of Musical Loudness and Gender of Listener. *Adv. Consum. Res.* **19,** 725–729 (1992).

57.   Arstila, V. Time slows down during accidents. *Front. Psychol.* **3,** (2012).

58.   Noyes, R. & Kletti, R. *Depersonalization in the face of life-threatening danger: a description.* Psychiatry **39,** 19–27 (1976).

59.   Campbell, L. A. & Bryant, R. A. How time flies: A study of novice skydivers. *Behav. Res. Ther.* **45,** 1389–1392 (2007).

60.   Stetson, C., Fiesta, M. P. & Eagleman, D. M. Does time really slow down during a frightening event? *PLoS One* **2,** (2007).

61.   Drummond, S. P. & Brown, G. G. The effects of total sleep deprivation on cerebral responses to cognitive performance. *Neuropsychopharmacology* **25,** S68-73 (2001).

62.   Dhand, R. & Sohal, H. Good sleep, bad sleep! The role of daytime

naps in healthy adults. *Curr. Opin. Intern. Med.* **6**, 91–94 (2007).

63. Rosekind, M. *et al.* Crew factors in flight operations IX: effects of planned cockpit rest on crew performance and alertness in long-haul operations. (1994). at <http://ntrs.nasa.gov/search.jsp?R=19950006379>

64. Schwarz, M. a, Winkler, I. & Sedlmeier, P. The heart beat does not make us tick: the impacts of heart rate and arousal on time perception. *Atten. Percept. Psychophys.* **75**, 182–193 (2013).

65. Hirano, Y. *et al.* Effects of chewing on cognitive processing speed. *Brain Cogn.* **81**, 376–381 (2013).

66. Verduyn, P. & Lavrijsen, S. Which emotions last longest and why: The role of event importance and rumination. *Motiv. Emot.* (2014). doi:10.1007/s11031-014-9445-y

67. Noulhiane, M., Mella, N., Samson, S., Ragot, R. & Pouthas, V. How emotional auditory stimuli modulate time perception. *Emotion* **7**, 697–704 (2007).

68. Buetti, S. & Lleras, A. Perceiving control over aversive and fearful events can alter how we experience those events: an investigation of time perception in spider-fearful individuals. *Front. Psychol.* **3**, 337 (2012).

69. Droit-Volet, S., Fayolle, S. L. & Gil, S. Emotion and time perception: effects of film-induced mood. *Front. Integr. Neurosci.* **5**, 33 (2011).

70. ANDERSON, M. J., REIS-COSTA, K. & MISANIN, J. R. Effects of September 11th Terrorism Stress on Estiamted Duration. *Percept. Mot. Skills* **104**, 799–802 (2007).

71. LANGER, J., WAPNER, S. & WERNER, H. The effect of danger upon the experience of time. *Am. J. Psychol.* **74**, 94–97 (1961).

72. Watts, F. N. & Sharrock, R. Fear and time estimation. *Percept. Mot. Skills* **59**, 597–598 (1984).

73. Tipples, J. Negative emotionality influences the effects of emotion on time perception. *Emotion* **8**, 127–131 (2008).

74. Gil, S., Niedenthal, P. M. & Droit-Volet, S. Anger and time perception in children. *Emotion* **7**, 219–225 (2007).

75. Mostofsky, E., Penner, E. A. & Mittleman, M. A. Outbursts of anger as a trigger of acute cardiovascular events: a systematic review and meta-analysis. *Eur. Heart J.* (2014).

76. Izard, C. E. & Ackerman, B. P. in *Handbook of emotions* xvi, 720 (2000).

77. Freed, P. J. & Mann, J. J. Sadness and Loss: Toward a Neurobiopsychosocial Model. 28–34 (2007).

78. Mezey, a. G. & Cohen, S. I. the Effect of Depressive Illness on

Time Judgment and Time Experience. *J. Neurol. Neurosurg. Psychiatry* **24**, 269–270 (1961).

79.   Sneed, R. S. & Cohen, S. A prospective study of volunteerism and hypertension risk in older adults. *Psychol. Aging* **28**, 578–586 (2013).

80.   Konrath, S., Fuhrel-Forbis, A., Lou, A. & Brown, S. Motives for volunteering are associated with mortality risk in older adults. *Heal. Psychol.* **31**, 87–96 (2012).

81.   Bar-Haim, Y., Kerem, A., Lamy, D. & Zakay, D. When time slows down: The influence of threat on time perception in anxiety. *Cogn. Emot.* **24**, 255–263 (2010).

82.   Wittmann, M., Vollmer, T., Schweiger, C. & Hiddemann, W. The relation between the experience of time and psychological distress in patients with hematological malignancies. *Palliat. Support. Care* **4**, 357–363 (2006).

83.   Twenge, J. M., Catanese, K. R. & Baumeister, R. F. Social exclusion and the deconstructed state: time perception, meaninglessness, lethargy, lack of emotion, and self-awareness. *J. Pers. Soc. Psychol.* **85**, 409–423 (2003).

84.   Bargh, J. A., Chen, M. & Burrows, L. Automaticity of social behavior: direct effects of trait construct and stereotype-activation on action. *J. Pers. Soc. Psychol.* **71**, 230–244 (1996).

85.   Thayer, S. & Schiff, W. Eye-contact, facial expression, and the experience of time. *J. Soc. Psychol.* **95**, 117–124 (1975).

86.   Effron, D. A., Niedenthal, P. M., Gil, S. & Droit-Volet, S. Embodied temporal perception of emotion. *Emotion* **6**, 1–9 (2006).

87.   MacLean, K. A., Johnson, M. W. & Griffiths, R. R. Mystical experiences occasioned by the hallucinogen psilocybin lead to increases in the personality domain of openness. *J. Psychopharmacol.* **25**, 1453–61 (2011).

88.   Rudd, M., Vohs, K. D. & Aaker, J. Awe expands people's perception of time, alters decision making, and enhances well-being. *Psychol. Sci.* **23**, 1130–6 (2012).

89.   Charles Darwin. *The Expression of the Emotions in Man and Animals.* (D. Appleton & Company, 1872).

90.   Endukuru, C. K., Maruthy, K. N. & Deepthi, T. S. A Study of Critical Flickering Fusion Frequency Rate in Media Players. **Volume: 2**, 499–502 (2015).

91.   Jackson, L. A. *et al.* Information technology use and creativity: Findings from the Children and Technology Project. *Comput. Human Behav.* **28**, 370–376 (2012).

92.   Kovess-Masfety, V. *et al.* Is time spent playing video games

associated with mental health, cognitive and social skills in young children? *Soc. Psychiatry Psychiatr. Epidemiol.* (2016). doi:10.1007/s00127-016-1179-6

93. Psychology Today. *Self-test* at <http://psychologytoday.tests.psychtests.com/take_test.php?idRegTest=1311>

94. Geen, R. G. Preferred stimulation levels in introverts and extroverts: Effects on arousal and performance.

95. Conte, J. M., Schwenneker, H. H., Dew, A. F. & Romano, D. M. Incremental Validity of Time Urgency and Other Type A Subcomponents in Predicting Behavioral and Health Criteria. *J. Appl. Soc. Psychol.* **31,** 1727–1748 (2001).

96. Locsin, R. C. Time experience of selected institutionalized adult clients. *Clin. Nurs. Res.* **2,** 452–463 (1993).

97. Esposito, M. J. *et al.* Prospective time estimation over a night without sleep. *Biological Rhythm Research* **38,** 443–450 (2007).

98. W. Christopher Winter. Sleep type predicts day and night batting averages of Major League Baseball players. *American Academy of Sleep Medicine (AASM)* (2011). at <http://www.aasmnet.org/articles.aspx?id=2306>

99. Wahlstrom, K. Changing Times: Findings from the First Longitudinal Study of Later High School Start Times. (2002).

100. Wieth, M. B. & Zacks, R. T. Time of day effects on problem solving: When the non-optimal is optimal. *Think. Reason.* **17,** 387–401 (2011).

101. O'Brien, E. H., Anastasio, P. A. & Bushman, B. J. Time crawls when you're not having fun: Feeling entitled makes dull tasks drag on. *Personal. Soc. Psychol. Bull.* **37,** 1287–1296 (2011).

102. Kakizaki, M. *et al.* Personality and body mass index: a cross-sectional analysis from the Miyagi Cohort Study. *J. Psychosom. Res.* **64,** 71–80 (2008).

103. Website. State-Trait Anxiety Inventory Online Test. *Self-Test* at <http://www.anxietytesting.com/anxiety-tests.php>

104. Murray, J. B. Marijuana's effects on human cognitive functions, psychomotor functions, and personality. *J. Gen. Psychol.* **113,** 23–55 (1986).

105. Lieving, L. M., Lane, S. D., Cherek, D. R. & Tcheremissine, O. V. Effects of marijuana on temporal discriminations in humans. *Behav. Pharmacol.* **17,** 173–83 (2006).

106. Harles T., T. Marijuana Intoxication: Common Experiences. *Nature* **226,** 701–704 (1970).

107. Perez-Reyes, M., Burstein, S. H., White, W. R., McDonald, S. A. &

Hicks, R. E. Antagonism of marihuana effects by indomethacin in humans. *Life Sci.* **48,** 507–15 (1991).

108.   Sewell, R. A. *et al.* Acute effects of THC on time perception in frequent and infrequent cannabis users. *Psychopharmacology (Berl).* **226,** 401–13 (2013).

109.   Matell, M. S., King, G. R. & Meck, W. H. Differential modulation of clock speed by the administration of intermittent versus continuous cocaine. *Behav. Neurosci.* **118,** 150–6 (2004).

110.   Bruce, M., Scott, N., Lader, M. & Marks, V. *The psychopharmacological and electrophysiological effects of single doses of caffeine in healthy human subjects. British Journal of Clinical Pharmacology* **22,** (1986).

111.   Rolland, B. *et al.* Pharmacology of hallucinations: several mechanisms for one single symptom? *Biomed Res. Int.* **2014,** 307106 (2014).

112.   Matell, M. S., Bateson, M. & Meck, W. H. Single-trials analyses demonstrate that increases in clock speed contribute to the methamphetamine-induced horizontal shifts in peak-interval timing functions. *Psychopharmacology (Berl).* **188,** 201–212 (2006).

113.   MacDonald, C. J. & Meck, W. H. Differential effects of clozapine and haloperidol on interval timing in the supraseconds range. *Psychopharmacology (Berl).* **182,** 232–244 (2005).

114.   Brozek, E. S. and J. Flicker Fusion Frequency: Background and Applications. *Physiol. Rev.* **32,** (1952).

115.   Hindmarch, I., Alford, C., Barwell, F. & Kerr, J. S. Measuring the side effects of psychotropics: the behavioural toxicity of antidepressants. *J. Psychopharmacol.* **6,** 198–203 (1992).

116.   Smith, A. P. Caffeine at work. *Hum. Psychopharmacol.* **20,** 441–5 (2005).

117.   Smith, A., Brice, C., Nash, J., Rich, N. & Nutt, D. J. Caffeine and central noradrenaline: effects on mood, cognitive performance, eye movements and cardiovascular function. *J. Psychopharmacol.* **17,** 283–92 (2003).

118.   Arushanyan, E. B., Baida, O. A., Mastyagin, S. S., Popova, A. P. & Shikina, I. B. Influence of Caffeine on the Subjective Perception of Time by Healthy Subjects in Dependence on Various Factors. *Hum. Physiol.* **29,** 433–436 (2003).

119.   Davranche, K. & Audiffren, M. Effects of a low dose of transdermal nicotine on information processing. *Nicotine Tob. Res.* **4,** 275–285 (2002).

120.   Turner, D. C. *et al.* Cognitive enhancing effects of modafinil in healthy volunteers. *Psychopharmacology (Berl).* **165,** 260–9 (2003).

121. Müller, U. *et al.* Effects of modafinil on non-verbal cognition, task enjoyment and creative thinking in healthy volunteers. *Neuropharmacology* **64,** 490–5 (2013).

122. Müller, U., Steffenhagen, N., Regenthal, R. & Bublak, P. Effects of modafinil on working memory processes in humans. *Psychopharmacology (Berl).* **177,** 161–9 (2004).

123. Baldwin, R. L. *et al.* Effect of methylphenidate on time perception in children with attention-deficit/hyperactivity disorder. *Exp. Clin. Psychopharmacol.* **12,** 57–64 (2004).

124. Allman, M. J. & Meck, W. H. Pathophysiological distortions in time perception and timed performance. *Brain* **135,** 656–77 (2012).

125. Coull, J. T., Cheng, R.-K. & Meck, W. H. Neuroanatomical and neurochemical substrates of timing. *Neuropsychopharmacology* **36,** 3–25 (2011).

126. Yang, B. *et al.* Time perception deficit in children with ADHD. *Brain Res.* **1170,** 90–96 (2007).

127. Curran, S. & Wattis, J. Critical flicker fusion threshold: A potentially useful measure for the early detection of Alzheimer's disease. *Hum. Psychopharmacol.* **15,** 103–112 (2000).

128. Bentivoglio, A. R. *et al.* Analysis of blink rate patterns in normal subjects. *Mov. Disord.* **12,** 1028–34 (1997).

129. Karson, C. N. Spontaneous eye-blink rates and dopaminergic systems. *Brain* **106 (Pt 3),** 643–53 (1983).

130. Kowal, M. A., Colzato, L. S. & Hommel, B. Decreased Spontaneous Eye Blink Rates in Chronic Cannabis Users: Evidence for Striatal Cannabinoid-Dopamine Interactions. *PLoS One* **6,** e26662 (2011).

131. Friedman, W. J. & Wilkins, A. J. Scale effects in memory for the time of events. *Mem. Cognit.* **13,** 168–175 (1985).

132. Brown, N. R., Rips, L. J. & Shevell, S. K. The subjective dates of natural events in very-long-term memory. *Cognitive Psychology* **17,** 139–177 (1985).

133. Whitten, W. B. & Leonard, J. M. Directed search through autobiographical memory. *Mem. Cognit.* **9,** 566–579 (1981).

134. Le Poidevin, R. The Experience and Perception of Time. *Stanford Encycl. Philos.* (2000). at <http://plato.stanford.edu/entries/time-experience/>

135. Ornstein, R. E. On the Experience of Time. (1969). at <http://philpapers.org/rec/ORNOTE>

136. Wackermann, J. Determinants of filled/empty optical illusion: differential effects of patterning. *Acta Neurobiol. Exp. (Wars).* **72,** 89–94 (2012).

137. Wearden, J. H., Norton, R., Martin, S. & Montford-Bebb, O. Internal clock processes and the filled-duration illusion. *J. Exp. Psychol. Hum. Percept. Perform.* **33,** 716–29 (2007).

138. Avni-Babad, D. & Ritov, I. *Routine and the perception of time. Journal of experimental psychology. General* **132,** (2003).

139. Zakay, D. Attention allocation policy influences prospective timing. *Psychon. Bull. Rev.* **5,** 114–118 (1998).

140. Block, R. a & Zakay, D. Prospective and retrospective duration judgments: A meta-analytic review. *Psychon. Bull. Rev.* **4,** 184–197 (1997).

141. Wearden, J. H. The wrong tree : time perception and time experience in the elderly. 134–156 (2005).

142. D'Argembeau, A., Renaud, O. & Van Der Linden, M. Frequency, characteristics and functions of future-oriented thoughts in daily life. *Appl. Cogn. Psychol.* **25,** 96–103 (2011).

143. Botzung, A., Denkova, E. & Manning, L. Experiencing past and future personal events: Functional neuroimaging evidence on the neural bases of mental time travel. *Brain Cogn.* **66,** 202–212 (2008).

144. Bilgin, B. & LeBoeuf, R. A. Looming Losses in Future Time Perception. *Journal of Marketing Research* **47,** 520–530 (2010).

145. Margolies, S. O. & Crawford, L. E. Event valence and spatial metaphors of time. *Cogn. Emot.* **22,** 1401–1414 (2008).

146. Scheier, M. F. *et al.* Dispositional optimism and recovery from coronary artery bypass surgery: the beneficial effects on physical and psychological well-being. *J. Pers. Soc. Psychol.* **57,** 1024–1040 (1989).

147. Patrick Fanning. *Visualization for Change.* (New Harbinger Publications, 1994).

148. Taylor, S. E., Pham, L. B., Rivkin, I. D. & Armor, D. A. Harnessing the imagination. Mental simulation, self-regulation, and coping. *The American psychologist* **53,** 429–439 (1998).

149. Konečni, V. J. & Ebbesen, E. B. Distortions of Estimates of Numerousness and Waiting Time. *J. Soc. Psychol.* **100,** 45–50 (1976).

150. Buehler, R., Griffin, D. & Ross, M. Exploring the 'planning fallacy': Why people underestimate their task completion times. *Journal of Personality and Social Psychology* **67,** 366–381 (1994).

151. Buehler, R. & Griffin, D. Planning, personality, and prediction: The role of future focus in optimistic time predictions. *Organ. Behav. Hum. Decis. Process.* **92,** 80–90 (2003).

152. Buehler, R., Griffin, D., Lam, K. C. H. & Deslauriers, J.

Perspectives on prediction: Does third-person imagery improve task completion estimates? *Organ. Behav. Hum. Decis. Process.* **117**, 138–149 (2012).

153. Gallant, R., Fidler, T. & Dawson, K. A. Subjective time estimation and age. *Percept. Mot. Skills* **72**, 1275–1280 (1991).

154. Joubert, C. E. Structured time and subjective acceleration of time. *Percept. Mot. Skills* **59**, 335–336 (1984).

155. Vanneste, S., Pouthas, V. & Wearden, J. H. Temporal Control of Rhythmic Performance: A Comparison Between Young and Old Adults. *Experimental Aging Research* **27**, 83–102 (2001).

156. Mangan, P. & P. Bolinskey. Underestimation of time during normal aging: The result of the slowing of a dopaminergic regulated internal clock? in *Annual Meeting of the Society for Neuroscience* (1997).

157. Wittmann, M. & Lehnhoff, S. Age effects in perception of time. *Psychol. Rep.* **97**, 921–935 (2005).

158. Friedman, W. J. & Janssen, S. M. J. Aging and the speed of time. *Acta Psychol. (Amst).* **134**, 130–41 (2010).

159. Rammsayer, T. H. Effects of body core temperature and brain dopamine activity on timing processes in humans. *Biol. Psychol.* **46**, 169–192 (1997).

160. Curran, S., Hindmarch, I., Wattis, J. P. & Shillingford, C. Critical flicker fusion in normal elderly subjects; a cross-sectional community study. *Curr. Psychol.* **9**, 25–34 (1990).

161. Lachenmayr, B. J. *et al.* The different effects of aging on normal sensitivity in flicker and light-sense perimetry. *Invest. Ophthalmol. Vis. Sci.* **35**, 2741–2748 (1994).

162. Carstensen, L. L. Evidence for a Life-Span Theory of Socioemotional Selectivity. *Current Directions in Psychological Science* **4**, 151–156 (1995).

163. Jiga-Boy, G. M., Clark, A. E. & Semin, G. R. So much to do and so little time. Effort and perceived temporal distance. *Psychol. Sci. a J. Am. Psychol. Soc. / APS* **21**, 1811–1817 (2010).

164. Tang, Y.-Y. *et al.* Short-term meditation training improves attention and self-regulation. *Proc. Natl. Acad. Sci. U. S. A.* **104**, 17152–6 (2007).

165. Davidson, R. J. *et al.* Alterations in brain and immune function produced by mindfulness meditation. *Psychosom. Med.* **65**, 564–570 (2003).

166. Li, P., Legault, J. & Litcofsky, K. a. Neuroplasticity as a function of second language learning: Anatomical changes in the human brain. *Cortex.* 1–24 (2014). doi:10.1016/j.cortex.2014.05.001

167. Van Boven, L. & Ashworth, L. Looking forward, looking back: anticipation is more evocative than retrospection. *J. Exp. Psychol. Gen.* **136,** 289–300 (2007).

168. Nawijn, J., Marchand, M. A., Veenhoven, R. & Vingerhoets, A. J. Vacationers Happier, but Most not Happier After a Holiday. *Appl. Res. Qual. Life* **5,** 35–47 (2010).

169. Tali Sharot. *The Optimism Bias: A Tour of the Irrationally Positive Brain.* (Pantheon, 2011).

ABOUT THE AUTHOR

Jean Paul Zogby, author of *The Power of Time Perception* is a writer, researcher, music composer, and real estate development expert.

His current passion is to help people understand why time speeds up and how to make the most of it. With the last 6 years spent researching Time Perception in the fields of **Neuroscience and Cognitive Psychology**, he is passionate about sharing what science has to say about our experience of time.

In his free time, Jean Paul composes soundtrack music for film and also publishes research related to the formation of planetary systems in the field of Astrophysics.

A husband and father of two lovely daughters and a son, he resides in Dubai where he is the CEO on a multi-billion construction project.

For more details, visit the Official Website at www.jpzogby.com where you can receive the **FREE** guide to a **Healthy Brain Diet** and **FREE** access to the online **Speed of Time test**

If you enjoyed this book or received value from it in any way, then I would like to ask if you would be kind enough to leave a review for this book on Amazon at the link below.

https://www.amazon.com/dp/B01MZEZL7S

It would be greatly appreciated!

CPSIA information can be obtained
at www.ICGtesting.com
Printed in the USA
BVOW08s0617211217
503258BV00002B/219/P